MAKING CONNECTIONS: Foundations for Algebra
Course 1, Version 2.0

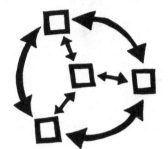

Managing Editors / Authors
Leslie Dietiker (Both Texts)
Michigan State University
East Lansing, MI

Evra Baldinger (Course 1)
Phillip and Sala Burton Academic High School
San Francisco, CA

Barbara Shreve (Course 2)
San Lorenzo High School
San Lorenzo, CA

Contributing Authors

Elizabeth Baker
Zane Middle School
Eureka, CA

Tara Bianchi
American Canyon Middle School
American Canyon, CA

Bev Brockhoff
Glen Edwards Middle School
Lincoln, CA

Mark Coté
Beaver Lake Middle School
Issaquah, WA

Suzanne Cisco Cox
Turner Middle School
Berthoud, CO

Kathleen Davies
Rincon Valley Middle School
Santa Rosa, CA

Josea Eggink
El Colegio Charter School
Minneapolis, MN

William Funkhouser
Zane Middle School
Eureka, CA

Brian Hoey
CPM Educational Program
Sacramento, CA

Janet Hollister
La Cumbre Jr. High School
Santa Barbara, CA

Carol Jancsi
Black Mountain Middle School
San Diego, CA

Rakesh Khanna
Hotmath, Inc.
Berkeley, CA

Judy Kysh, Ph.D.
San Francisco State University
San Francisco, CA

Bruce Melhorn
Whatcom Middle School
Bellingham, WA

Chris Mikles
Post Falls Middle School
Post Falls, ID

Misty Nikula
Whatcom Day Academy
Bellingham, WA

Bob Petersen
CPM Educational Program
Sacramento, CA

Tom Sallee, Ph.D.
Department of Mathematics
University of California, Davis

Lorna Thomas Vázquez
Math Consultant
Neillsville, WI

Stephanie Whitney
University of Minnesota
Minneapolis, MN

Illustrators

Rebecca Bobell
Kevin Coffey
Eli Marable
Jonathan Weast

Technical Managers

Sarah Maile
Sacramento, CA

Aubrie Maze
Sebastopol, CA

Technical Assistants

Robert Ainsworth
Hannah Coyner
Bethany Firch
Eli Marable
Atlanta Parrott
Alex Yu

Rebecca Bobell
Carmen de la Cruz
Michael Li
Aubrie Maze
John Ramos

Jason Cho
Matthew Donahue
Jerry Luo
James McCardle
Rachel Smith

Program Directors

Leslie Dietiker
Michigan State University
East Lansing, MI

Brian Hoey
CPM Educational Program
Sacramento, CA

Judy Kysh, Ph.D.
Departments of Education and Mathematics
San Francisco State University, CA

Tom Sallee, Ph.D.
Department of Mathematics
University of California, Davis

1 2 3 4 5 6 7 8 9   12 11 10 09   Version 2.0

Printed in the United States of America   ISBN-13: 978-1-60328-022-8

Making Connections: Foundations for Algebra
Course 1
Student Edition
Version 2.0

Similarity, Multiplying Fractions, and Equivalence

6

CHAPTER 6 Similarity, Multiplying Fractions, and Equivalence

You will begin this chapter by working with your class to enlarge a mystery mascot. Then you will learn how to enlarge or reduce figures while keeping their shape consistent. You will use ratios to **compare** the side lengths of figures and develop your ability to estimate fractions and predict sizes of enlargements using ratios.

In Section 6.2, you will calculate portions of fractions, or "parts of parts." You will use these ideas to develop strategies for multiplying fractions, mixed numbers, and decimals.

Finally, in Section 6.3, your new knowledge of multiplying fractions will make it possible for you to learn a powerful new tool for finding equivalent fractions and ratios. This new tool can be used to test whether two fractions or ratios are equivalent and it will also help you convert any fraction to a percent.

Guiding Questions

Think about these questions throughout this chapter:

How can I change the size but keep the shape the same?

How is it the same or different?

How can I visualize it?

Is there another way to see it?

In this chapter, you will learn:

➤ How to enlarge and reduce figures while maintaining their shape.

➤ How to use ratios to **describe** relationships between similar shapes.

➤ What kind of growth is needed to maintain a shape.

➤ How to calculate a part of another part.

➤ How to multiply fractions, mixed numbers and decimals.

➤ A useful tool for finding equivalent fractions.

➤ How to convert any fraction to an equivalent percent.

Chapter Outline

Section 6.1 In this section, you will learn how to enlarge and reduce figures while maintaining their shape. You will also learn about using ratios to **describe** relationships between shapes of different sizes.

Section 6.2 In Section 6.2, you will learn how to multiply fractions by examining portions of fractions. You will also learn how this process can be connected to finding the products of other portions, including mixed numbers and decimals.

Section 6.3 In the final section of this chapter, you will develop a powerful tool for finding equivalent fractions and verifying equivalence. You will also learn how to convert any fraction to a percent.

Making Connections: Course 1

6.1.1 How can I enlarge a shape?

Enlarging Two-Dimensional Shapes

How do muralists create pictures that are so large that you can only see them from a distance? In most cases, designs for large projects like murals are first created as small pieces of art and then enlarged to fit the larger space to be painted. In this lesson, you will work with your class to enlarge a design that could turn into a mural.

6-1.   MYSTERY MASCOT

Jeremy and Julie are members of the spirit club of JFK Middle School. They have been given permission to paint a mural of their school mascot on the wall of the gym. To make the mascot look right, they have decided to cut up a small picture of the mascot and enlarge each of the pieces before putting the pieces back together. They need your help.

Your task: Obtain a part of the mural and an enlargement grid from your teacher. Draw your section of the mural so that it fills the large grid yet still looks the same as the part of the mural on your sample. Work with your teammates to ensure that everyone's drawings are as accurate as possible.

When all parts of the picture are completed, work with your class to put them together to make the mascot mural. What is the mascot of JFK Middle School?

6-2.   Your teacher will assign your team a part of the mascot to measure.
For example, your part might be a foot or an eye. For the part that you are
assigned, measure it on the original mascot and then on the corresponding part
of the enlarged mascot.

a.   Work with your class to share data and
complete a table like the one at right.

mascot part	original (cm)	enlarged (cm)

b.   With your team, examine the data collected by
your team. Look for a way to **describe** the
relationship between parts of the original
mascot and the enlarged mascot. Be prepared to share your ideas with the
class.

c.   Is there any part of the enlarged mural that seems to be the wrong size?
How could you check?

6-3.   How much bigger did the mascot get? Work with your team to find a way to
describe how much bigger the mascot mural is than the original drawing. Be
prepared to **explain** your ideas to the class.

6-4.   On grid paper, draw a simple design inside of a 5×5 square. Then enlarge
your picture as accurately as possible so that it fits inside of a 15×15 square.
How much wider and how much longer is your new picture?

6-5.   Armando and Vlad were flipping three coins: a nickel, a dime, and a quarter.

a.   Make an organized list of all of the possible outcomes. If the nickel comes
up heads, the dime comes up heads, and the quarter comes up tails, we
write this outcome as HHT.

b.   They decided that Armando would win when exactly two heads came up
and Vlad would win when exactly one head came up. Who has a better
chance of winning? **Explain.**

Making Connections: Course 1

6-6.   Jenna was building a pen for her new sheep. She needs a total of 40 linear feet of lumber. Some of her neighbors have agreed to give her lumber and she wants to know if she has enough.

a.   Neighbor Jim will give her a board that he says is $8\frac{1}{2}$ feet long. Neighbor Malia will give her two boards that she says are each 126 inches long. What is the total length of Jenna's lumber?

b.   Neighbor Mike called and offered to donate a board that is 400 centimeters long. Jenna found the conversion information at right. Help her to figure out if she has enough lumber to make her pen.

1 cm = 0.3937 in
1 m = 3.281 ft
100 cm = 1 m

6-7.   Complete the web shown at right to represent the portion 105% as a fraction, a decimal, and with a description.

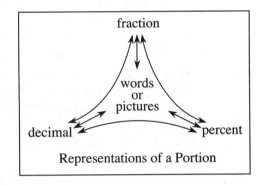

6-8.   **Describe** *at least* two **different ways** that you could add 744 and 304 without writing anything down.

6.1.2 How does it change?

Enlarging and Reducing Figures

In Lesson 6.1.1, you worked with your class to enlarge an image while maintaining its overall shape. You began to **describe** what happens to each part of a shape when it is enlarged this way. In this lesson, you will identify shapes that have been enlarged and reduced correctly and those that have been enlarged or reduced incorrectly. You will also use your new understanding to enlarge and reduce shapes of your own.

6-9.   THE BROKEN COPIER

   The social studies teachers at CPM Middle School are working together to plan a geography unit. They are using all of the school's copy machines to enlarge and reduce images from books to make them convenient sizes. The teachers suspect that some of the copy machines might be broken and are not making accurate copies of the original images.

   Your task: Obtain the Lesson 6.1.2 Resource Page from your teacher. Work with your team to identify which, if any, of the images have been made using a broken copier. Be ready to **explain** how you can be sure if any of the copies are incorrect.

6-10.   Carmen and Dolores want to enlarge the triangle at right. They want the base of their new triangle to be 12 units long, and they want the shape of the new triangle to stay the same. However, they disagree about what the new triangle's height should be.

   a.   Work with your team to predict the height of the new triangle.

   b.   Carmen noticed that the base grew by 9 units, so she is sure that the height of the new triangle should be 9 units longer, or 17 units high. Dolores noticed that the base got four *times* longer, so she is sure that the height of the new triangle should be four times longer, or 32 units high.

      i.   On graph paper, draw the original triangle as well as the triangles that Carmen and Dolores propose.

      ii.   Who is correct? How can you tell?

   c.   What if Carmen and Dolores wanted to reduce the shape so that the base of the new smaller triangle would be 1 unit long? How high should the triangle be to keep its original shape? How did you figure this out?

6-11.   Since some of the copiers at JFK Middle School are broken, the math teachers plan to do all of their reductions and enlargements by hand. They need your team's help. Using grid paper, draw each of the original figures described in parts (a) and (b) below and enlarge or reduce them as described.

      a.   Draw a rectangle that measures 5 units by 3 units. Enlarge it so that each side is four times as long as the original.

      b.   Draw a right triangle with a base of 2 units and a height of 3 units. Make three "copies" so that the lengths of the sides of the resulting shapes are 50%, 300%, and 500% of the lengths of the corresponding sides of the original.

6-12.   LEARNING LOG

Work with your team to **describe** how you can tell if an image has been enlarged correctly. When you have come to an agreement, write your ideas as a Learning Log entry. Title this entry "Enlarging Figures" and label it with today's date.

6-13.   Draw three different simple geometric shapes (such at rectangles or right triangles) on grid paper.

      a.   Choose one shape and enlarge it so that each side is twice as long as the original.

      b.   Choose another shape and reduce it so that each side is half the length of the original.

      c.   Enlarge the original shape you used in part (b) so that each side is 2.5 times the length of the original.

6-14.   Include a sketch to support each of your answers below.

      a.   How many fifths are there in a whole?

      b.   How many thirds are there in $2\frac{1}{3}$?

      c.   How many $\frac{2}{5}$ are there in 4?

      d.   How could you represent each of the questions in parts (a) through (c) and their answers as division problems?

6-15.   Simplify each expression.

    a. $6+(-2)$ b. $-7+(-7)$ c. $1+(-4)$

    d. $-42+11+(-3)$ e.   5 groups of (-6) f. $7(-4)$

6-16.   At right is a stem-and-leaf plot for the weight of each book in
Jenna's backpack, measured in ounces. For example, she has a
journal that weighs 12 ounces and a history book that weighs
35 ounces. After third period, Jenna realized that she had left
her science book (64 oz) and her paperback novel (11 oz) at
home. Her mother agreed to bring them to her at lunch.

1	2 8
2	0 6 9
3	5 5
4	
5	
6	

Think about how the addition of the two books will change the
measures of central tendency of the weights in her backpack.
Which will increase, decrease, or stay the same? For each part below, fill in the
word or phrase that best **describes** the change and write the complete sentence.
For each one, **explain** how you can tell *without* calculating.

    a.   The mean will _____ .   b.   The median will _____ .

    c.   The mode will _____ .   d.   The range will _____ .

    e.   Calculate each measure of central tendency (mean, median, and mode) and
the range to test your predictions.

6-17.   Maria was putting together party favors for her niece's birthday party. In each
bag she put three small chocolate candies and four hard candies.

    a.   How many candies did she put in each bag?

    b.   If Maria had 10 bags, how many candies did she use in all?

    c.   In order to represent the total number of candies in ten bags, we write the
expression $10 \cdot (3+4)$. What expression would we write to represent the
total number of candies used if Maria had to make 12 bags for party favors?

6.1.3 How can I compare them?

Enlargement and Reduction Ratios

In the past few lessons, you have enlarged and reduced images while preserving their shape. You learned, for example, that to enlarge a shape to 300% of the original, you multiplied the length of each side by 3.

In this lesson, you will learn about using **ratios**, a useful way to **compare** lengths of sides to determine whether enlargements or reductions were done correctly. As you work with your team, use the questions below to help start your discussions.

How does the shape change?

What are we **comparing**?

How can we **describe** the relationship?

6-18.   Andrew, Barb, Carlos, and Dolores noticed the two triangles shown at right that were made on the school's copier. *"I'm confused,"* said Carlos, *"Is the one on the right an enlargement of the one on the left, or is the one on the left a reduction of the one on the right?"* To help them **compare** the triangles, they placed a grid on each shape, as shown at right.

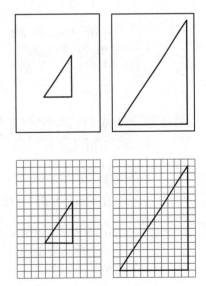

   a.   Work with your team to find a way to **describe** the relationship between the lengths of the sides of these two triangles. Think about how each triangle might have been created from the other one. Be prepared to share your ideas with the class.

Problem continues on next page →

6-18.   *Problem continued from previous page.*

    b.   *"Hey,"* Barb said, *"I just learned about* **ratios** *from my sister. She told me that ratios are another way to* **compare** *quantities like the dimensions of these triangles. We could* **compare** *these triangles by setting up the ratio of 4 units to 10 units. We can write it in these ways."*

$$4 : 10$$
$$\frac{4}{10}$$
$$4 \text{ to } 10$$

        Carlos wondered, *"But, wait. Why wouldn't the ratio be 6 to 15?"*

        i.   Where did Barb and Carlos get the numbers that they are using in their ratios? What are they **comparing**?

        ii.   Whose ratio is correct? How do you know?

        iii.   What are some other ratios that are the same as Barb's? Work with your team to find at least three other ratios and be prepared to share them with the class.

    c.   Dolores was confused and wondered out loud, *"Why isn't the ratio 10:4?"* What do you think?

6-19.   After listening to his team's discussion about ratios, Andrew said that he thought about the relationship between the triangles in another way. He drew the diagram at right on his paper to show his team.

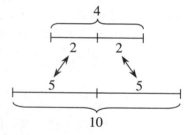

    a.   What idea could Andrew be trying to show with his diagram?

    b.   Does Andrew's thinking seem to agree with Barb and Carlos in problem 6-18? Why or why not?

    c.   Use a diagram like Andrew's to show the relationship between the heights of the triangles. How does this ratio **compare** to the ratio for the bases?

6-20.   Work on grid paper to draw any quadrilateral with one side that is 12 units long and another side that is 9 units long. Then reduce your quadrilateral so that the ratio of sides of new to original is 2 to 3.

6-21.   Xenia drew the trapezoid at right. She wanted to draw another figure of the same shape so that the relationship between the two figures could be **described** by the ratio of 2 to 7 or $\frac{2}{7}$. What will be the length of the longest side (the base) of her new shape? Is there **more than one** possibility for her new shape?

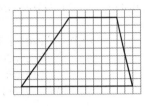

6-22.   TEAM CHALLENGE

Carlos was working with his team to solve the following challenge problem.

Triangles A, B, and C are shown in the figure at right. The ratio of the sides of triangle A to triangle B is the same as the ratio of the sides of triangle B to triangle C.

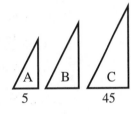

Carlos says that the base of triangle B must be 25 units long, because 25 is halfway between 5 and 45. Is he correct? If so, **explain** how you can be sure. If not, what *is* the length of the base of triangle B? How do you know?

6-23.   Does the ratio of areas of enlargements stay the same as well? Think about this as you conduct the following investigation.

a.   Find the area and perimeter of the rectangle at right.

b.   Draw a new rectangle that is an enlargement of rectangle above, so that the ratio of the sides of the original rectangle to the new one is 2:3 and label the length and width.

c.   Find the area and perimeter of the new larger rectangle.

d.   Write the ratio of the original perimeter to new perimeter and the original area to new area. Are the ratios the same?

6-24.   LEARNING LOG

Today you learned about a different way to show **comparisons**, with a ratio. Write a Learning Log entry **describing** what you know so far about ratios including the different ways that they can be written. Include an example of how you can use a ratio to enlarge or reduce a figure. Title this entry "Ratios" and label it with today's date.

6-25. On grid paper, draw any quadrilateral. Then enlarge it by each of the following ratios.

   a. $\frac{4}{1}$ b. $\frac{7}{2}$

6-26. What portion of one dollar is represented by each of the following sets of coins? Express you answers as fractions and percents.

   a. One quarter   b. Three dimes   c. Eight nickels

   d. 23 pennies   e. Five quarters   f. Nine dimes

6-27. Dante went to the grocery store and bought a 5-pound bag of oranges and 40 ounces of cheese. How much do his groceries weigh? (Note that there are 16 ounces in a pound.)

6-28. Molly and Nancy are having a disagreement about the value of the expression $2 + 3 \cdot 4$. Molly thinks it is 20 and Nancy thinks it is 14. How could each of them have calculated their answer? Who is correct?

6-29. Ms. Jancsi bought a new package (containing 300 inches) of border decoration to put around the bulletin board in her classroom. The dimensions of the rectangular bulletin board are 8 feet by 3 feet. If she puts the border around all four sides of the bulletin board, how much will she have left over? Include a labeled sketch in your answer.

6-30. Use a generic rectangle to multiply 467(392).

6.1.4 How can I use ratios?

Ratios in Other Contexts

In the previous lesson, you used ratios to **describe** and **compare** the lengths of sides of figures that had been reduced or enlarged. Is this the only way that ratios can be used? In this lesson, you will expand your use of ratios to contexts that do not involve geometric figures and find that this way of **describing** the relationship between two different quantities is a valuable tool for **making sense** of and solving problems. As you work with your team, keep the following question in mind: What is being **compared**?

6-31.   Katura was making Algebr-Ade drink from a bag of powdered mix for her sister. The directions said to use 5 scoops of the powder for every 8 cups of water. Since she knows that it will be a very hot day and that her sister will drink a lot, she decides that she will use 12 cups of water. She knows that if she does not figure out the right amount of powder to add, then her sister will not drink it.

a. What is the ratio of powder to water in the original? When Katura figures out the ratio for the larger amount of mixture, how should this **compare** to the original ratio?

b. Work with your team to draw a diagram or use another method of your choice to represent the ratio of Algebr-Ade powder to water in the original directions and to figure out how much powder Katura needs to mix with 12 cups of water. Try to find **more than one way** to **describe** or show how you know that your answer **makes sense**. Be prepared to **explain** your ideas to the class.

6-32.   ON THE TRAIL AGAIN

Ms. Hartley's students were working with their mix of raisins and peanuts from Chapters 1 and 4. The class found that 30% of the mix was raisins. Sophie was working with a sample from the mix and counted 42 peanuts in it.

Sophie had just poured her sample back into the jar, when she realized that she had counted the wrong thing! Her teacher wanted to know how many *raisins* were in the samples, not *peanuts*! Work with your team to use ratios to help Sophie fix her mistake.

Problem continues on next page →

6-32.   *Problem continued from previous page.*

    a.   Sophie knows that 30% is the same as $\frac{30}{100}$. Can this be thought of as a ratio? Which two quantities are being **compared** in this case? Can you write another equivalent ratio representing the same **comparison**?

    b.   Could Sophie write a ratio **comparing** the number of raisins to peanuts? How could you figure out this ratio without having to count the peanuts? Discuss this with your team and be ready to **explain** your thinking to the class.

    c.   Find an equivalent ratio that will help Sophie figure out how many raisins should have been in her sample that contained 42 peanuts.

6-33.   Nicci has a bag of colored blocks with 5 blue blocks, 4 red blocks, 2 yellow blocks, and 1 green block.

    a.   Find the following ratios for Nicci's bag of blocks:

       i.   The number of blue blocks to total blocks

       ii.   The number of blue blocks to the number of red blocks

       iii.   The number of blue blocks to the combined number of red and green blocks.

    b.   Which of the ratios above would be helpful to determine the probability of selecting a blue block from the bag?

    c.   If Nicci combines her bag with another identical bag, what happens to each of the ratios that you wrote in part (a)? That is, how will the new ratios that you would write for the combined bags **compare** to the ones you wrote for the original bag?

6-34.   Poor Trei got a 60% on her last spelling test!

    a.   How many words did she spell correctly for each word that she spelled wrong? That is, what is her ratio of correctly to incorrectly spelled words?

    b.   Stan spelled 3 words correctly for every 1 that he missed. Did Stan do better than Trei on the test? What is Stan's score represented as a percent?

METHODS AND MEANINGS

MATH NOTES

Ratios

A **ratio** is a comparison of two amounts. A ratio can be written in words, as a fraction, or with colon notation. Most often in this class we will write ratios as fractions or state them in words.

For example, if there are 38 students in the school band and 16 of them are boys, we can write the ratio of the number of boys to the number of girls as:

16 boys to 22 girls $\frac{16 \text{ boys}}{22 \text{ girls}}$ 16 boys : 22 girls

6-35.   Michael and Elizabeth play basketball and practice shooting free throws after school. During one practice session, Michael shot 15 free throws and made 12.

    a.   Write a ratio to how the number of free throws he made **compared** the number that he missed.

    b.   Elizabeth made eight free throws for every 3 that she missed. Did Elizabeth do better than Michael? Show how you know.

6-36.   Answer each of the questions below.

    a.   How many fourths are in $4\frac{1}{4}$? Use your answer to rewrite $4\frac{1}{4}$ in the form $\frac{\square}{4}$.

    b.   How many thirds are in $3\frac{2}{3}$? Use your answer to rewrite $3\frac{2}{3}$ in the form $\frac{\square}{3}$.

6-37.   Simplify each expression.

       a. $-2-0$ b. $0-(-4)$ c. $0-2$

       d. $-8-(-6)$ e. $-8-6$ f. $8-(-6)$

       g. $-15-4$ h. $-15-(-4)$ i. $15-(-4)$

6-38.   Ashley painted $\frac{1}{2}$ of her bathroom ceiling. Alex painted $\frac{1}{4}$ of the ceiling in the school library.

$\frac{1}{2}$ of bathroom ceiling

       a. Who painted the larger fraction of their ceiling?

       b. If the drawings at right accurately represent the relationship between the ceiling sizes, who painted more ceiling area?

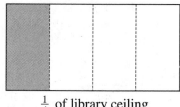

$\frac{1}{4}$ of library ceiling

       c. **Explain** why the answers for parts (a) and (b) should be different.

6-39.   The high temperatures for six Saturdays were 78°, 92°, 86°, 95°, 64°, and 89°.

       a. What is the mean high temperature for those Saturdays?

       b. What is the median high temperature for those Saturdays?

6.2.1 How can I describe it?

Analyzing Parts of Parts

In this section, you will use the understanding of portions that you have gained throughout this course to develop strategies for finding parts of parts.

6-40.   MURAL MADNESS

Riley, Morgan, and Reggie were planning a mural on the side of a community center and they needed to clean and prime the wall. Riley agreed to prepare $\frac{1}{2}$ of the area, Morgan agreed to do $\frac{1}{3}$ of the area, while Reggie agreed to the remaining $\frac{1}{6}$ of the area.

A few days later, none of them had completed all of his or her section. Riley had completed $\frac{1}{3}$ of his part. Morgan had completed $\frac{5}{6}$ of her part. Reggie had completed $\frac{2}{3}$ of his part.

Your first task: Obtain a Lesson 6.2.1 Resource Page and work with your team to decide who has completed the least of the total mural area and who has completed the most. Be prepared to defend your conclusions to the class in as many ways as you can.

Your second task: Your teacher will assign your team one student's section to analyze. With your team, figure out what fraction of the whole mural space your student has finished preparing. Be prepared to share your strategies with the class.

Discussion Points

How can we draw a diagram to help us **compare** the parts?

Does anyone **see it in another way**?

6-41.   On your Lesson 6.2.1 Resource Page, represent each student's portion of the mural. Work with your team to decide who has painted more. Be prepared to **explain** your decision in as many ways as possible.

6-42.   Obtain a new Lesson 6.2.1 Resource Page from your teacher and draw a diagram of Riley's, Morgan's, or Reggie's section. Can you find **more than one way** to do this?

       a.   Find **at least two ways** to divide the mural into pieces so that you can count how many of these pieces your student has completed.

       b.   Write your student's portion as a fraction in the form $\frac{\text{pieces painted}}{\text{total pieces in mural}}$.

*Further Guidance
section ends here.*

6-43.   Janine drew the square diagram at right as she was working on Riley's portion of "Mural Madness" (problem 6-40). Her brother James looked over her shoulder and said, *"Oh, you're learning about area?"*

"Why do you say that?" Janine asked.

He answered, *"It looks like you have shaded a rectangle with a length of $\frac{1}{3}$ unit and a width of $\frac{1}{2}$ unit, and you have shaded its area."*

Is James right? What is the area of the darkly shaded rectangle in Janine's diagram? Write the area as a product of length and width.

6-44.   For each product below, choose one of the diagrams at right that might be useful. Copy the diagram on your own paper and complete it to find the product.

       a. $\frac{3}{4} \cdot \frac{1}{3}$ b. $\frac{1}{5} \cdot \frac{1}{7}$

       c. $\frac{3}{7} \cdot \frac{2}{5}$ d. $\frac{4}{4} \cdot \frac{2}{3}$

Making Connections: Course 1

6-45.   The diagrams below show the portion of another class mural that Josephine was supposed to paint and how much she actually did paint. Use the pictures to answer the questions that follow.

The portion Josephine was supposed to paint:

The portion Josephine actually painted:

a.   Approximately what portion of the painting was Josephine supposed to paint?

b.   Approximately what fraction of her assigned portion did Josephine actually complete?

c.   Write a product to show what portion of the mural Josephine actually painted.

6-46.   Recall that a factor of a number divides it evenly. For example, 4 and 6 are factors of 12.

a.   Find all the factors of 24.

b.   Find the smallest number that has 1, 2, 3, 4, and 5 as factors.

c.   Find the second smallest number that has 1, 2, 3, 4, and 5 as factors.

6-47.   Answer each of the questions below.

a.   How many eighths are in $5\frac{5}{8}$? Use your answer to rewrite $5\frac{5}{8}$ in the form $\frac{\square}{8}$.

b.   How many fifths are in $6\frac{4}{5}$? Use your answer to rewrite $6\frac{4}{5}$ in the form $\frac{\square}{5}$.

6-48.   Draw a rectangle with a width of 8 units and a length of 6 units.

   a.   What is the enlargement ratio if you enlarge the figure to have a width of 16 units and a length of 12 units?

   b.   If you wanted to reduce the rectangle by a ratio of $\frac{1}{4}$, what would the dimensions of the new rectangle be?

6-49.   Multiple Choice: If the experimental probability of getting a particular result in an experiment is 75.3%, what is the probability of *not* getting that result?

   A. $75.3\% + 100\%$ B. $75.3\% - 100\%$

   C. $100\% - 75.3\%$ D. $\frac{1}{75.3\%}$

6-50.   Arrange each of these fractions on a number line: $\frac{5}{8}, \frac{3}{16}, \frac{3}{8}, \frac{16}{16}, \frac{1}{4}, \frac{1}{8}, \frac{3}{4}, \frac{7}{8}$.

6.2.2 How big is it?

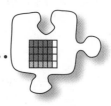

Calculating a Portion of a Fraction

In Chapter 4, you used percents, fractions, and decimals to represent portions of wholes. In this lesson, you will find a portion of a fraction. As a team, you will create a complete **description** of how to show and name a portion of a fraction. As you work with your team, ask the following questions:

How can we show a part of a fraction?

Is there another way to show it?

How does this portion relate to the whole?

6-51. TEAM CHALLENGE: Parts of Parts, Part One

Representing a portion of a fraction can be thought of as finding a "part of a part." For each of the parts of parts described in parts (a) through (c) below, work with your team to figure out what part of the whole is described. For each problem, show at least one picture or diagram that helps you to **make sense** of the problem.

a. $\frac{3}{5}$ of $\frac{2}{7}$ b. $\frac{2}{3} \cdot 2$

6-52. Grant, Oliver and Sonya were working on the problem below.

Jenny's house is $\frac{4}{7}$ of a mile from the bus stop. If Jenny had to run $\frac{2}{3}$ of the way from her house to the bus stop, what portion of a mile did Jenny run?

They each started by **visualizing** $\frac{4}{7}$ in their own way. Each of their diagrams is shown below.

Grant's Drawing: Oliver's Drawing: Sonya's Drawing

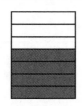   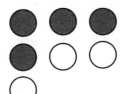   

Problem continues on next page →

Chapter 6: Similarity, Multiplying Fractions, and Equivalence   291

6-52.   *Problem continued from previous page.*

   a.   Copy all three diagrams and work with your team to figure out how to use each diagram to show $\frac{2}{3}$ of $\frac{4}{7}$.

   b.   Which of the three drawings do you prefer to use? **Explain** why you chose the drawing that you did.

   c.   What fraction of a whole is $\frac{2}{3} \cdot \frac{4}{7}$?

6-53.   **Additional Challenge:** Work with your team to calculate each of the following products. Draw a diagram to show your thinking for each part.

   a. $\frac{2}{9}$ of 80% of the area of a mural   b. $\frac{2}{3} \cdot 2\frac{7}{8}$

METHODS AND MEANINGS

Mixed Numbers and Fractions Greater than One

MATH NOTES

The number $4\frac{1}{4}$ is called a **mixed number** because it is composed of a whole number, 4, and a fraction, $\frac{1}{4}$.

The number $\frac{17}{4}$ is called a **fraction greater than one** because the numerator is larger than the denominator so its value is greater than one. (Sometimes such fractions are called improper fractions, but this is just an historical term. There is nothing wrong with the fractions themselves.)

The fraction $\frac{17}{4}$ is equal in value to $4\frac{1}{4}$.

Depending upon which arithmetic operations you are performing, you will want to choose whether to write your number as a mixed number or a fraction greater than one.

6-54. Grace and William were wondering if *one half of a third* would be the same as *one third of a half*.

    a.   Draw a picture that shows one half of one third.

    b.   Draw a picture that shows one third of one half.

    c.   Write a note to Grace and William explaining how these two values **compare** and why the result **makes sense**.

6-55. George drew the diagram at right to represent the number $2\frac{2}{5}$. *"Look,"* said Helena, *"This is the same thing as $\frac{12}{5}$."*

    a.   Is Helena correct? If so, **explain** how she can tell that the diagram represents $\frac{12}{5}$. If she is not correct, **explain** why not.

    b.   Draw a diagram to represent the **mixed number** $3\frac{2}{3}$. How can you write this as a single fraction greater than one?

    c.   How can you write $\frac{7}{4}$ as a mixed number? Be sure to include a diagram in your answer.

6-56. Ms. Whitney has eight students who did extra credit assignments to raise their grades. The scores on the assignments were 45, 100, 100, 67, 98, 33, 60, and 100.

    a.   Make a stem-and-leaf plot of this data.

    b.   Find the median and the mode.

6-57. Find each of the parts of parts described below. For each one, create a diagram that demonstrates your thinking.

    a. $\frac{3}{4}$ of $\frac{5}{8}$ b. $\frac{3}{8}\cdot\frac{2}{3}$ c. $\frac{2}{3}$ of $\frac{7}{8}$ d. $\frac{4}{5}\cdot\frac{3}{7}$

6-58. Copy and complete each of the Diamond Problems below. The pattern used in the Diamond Problems is shown at right.

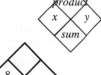

    a.   b.   c.

6.2.3 How can I calculate it without drawing?

Multiplying Fractions

In the past few lessons, you have worked with your teammates and your class to develop multiple strategies for finding parts of parts, that is, for multiplying fractions. In some situations, you may want a method for multiplying fractions without needing to draw a diagram, so in this lesson you will find strategies for doing this. As you work with your team, use the following questions to help focus your discussion.

How can we **visualize** it?

How many parts should there be?

What is the portion of the whole?

6-59. How can you figure out the size of a part of a part without having to draw a diagram? Work with your team or your class to explore this question as you consider the example of $\frac{2}{3} \cdot \frac{5}{7}$.

a. **Describe** how you would draw a diagram to make this calculation.

b. If the diagram were to be completed, how many parts would there be in all? How do you know?

c. How many of the parts would be counted for the numerator of your result? Again, **describe** how you know.

d. How could you know what the numerator and denominator of a product will be without having to draw or envision a diagram each time? Discuss this with your team and be prepared to **explain** your ideas to the class.

6-60. Autumn wants to multiply $\frac{5}{9} \cdot 4$ without having to draw a diagram. Work with your team to figure out how Autumn's expression can be written with two fractions, and then find the product.

6-61. TEAM CHALLENGE: Parts of Parts, part 2

Work with your team to find each of the following parts of parts *without drawing a diagram*. For each problem, **explain** clearly why your answer **makes sense**.

a. $\frac{2}{3}$ of $\frac{4}{5}$ b. $\frac{6}{11} \cdot \frac{2}{7}$ c. $\frac{2}{5}$ of 70% d. $3\frac{1}{5} \cdot \frac{2}{3}$

6-62. Each of the following pairs of diagrams shows a first and second step that could be used to represent a multiplication problem. For each pair, write a multiplication problem and its solution. Be prepared to share your ideas with the class.

a.

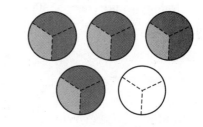

b.

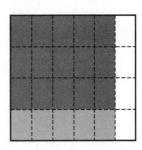

c.

d.

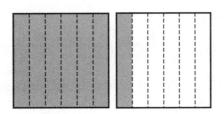 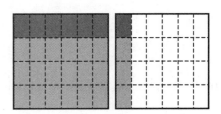

6-63.   Andy and Bill were working on finding $\frac{1}{3}$ of $\frac{3}{8}$. They
started by drawing the diagram at right. Suddenly Andy
had an idea. *"Wait!"* he said, *"I can see the answer in this
diagram without having to draw anything else."*

a.   Discuss with your team what Andy might have been
talking about. Be prepared to share your ideas with
the class.

b.   Work with your team to find other examples of fractions that could be
multiplied using a simple diagram like Andy's.

6-64.   LEARNING LOG

In your Learning Log, **describe** a strategy for multiplying
fractions. Use examples and diagrams to **explain** why this
strategy **makes sense**. Title this entry, "Multiplying
Fractions" and label it with today's date.

6-65.   Multiple Choice: Which of the following numbers could not represent a
probability? Write a sentence explaining why.

A. $-\frac{1}{10}$ B.   1   C.   1%   D.   0.1

6-66.   Write each of the mixed numbers below as fractions greater than one, and the
fractions greater than one as mixed numbers. Include a diagram to **explain**
each answer.

a. $4\frac{1}{3}$ b. $\frac{15}{4}$ c. $3\frac{1}{2}$ d. $\frac{15}{8}$

6-67.   Calculate each of the following parts of parts.

a. $\frac{2}{3}$ of $\frac{3}{7}$ b. $\frac{1}{2}$ of $\frac{3}{5}$

6-68.   Draw a number line and place each of the following fractions in its appropriate
place on the line: $-5\frac{1}{2}$, -2, $4\frac{3}{4}$, 6, -1, $\frac{3}{2}$, -0.5.

6-69.   Simplify the following expressions.

a. $-8+(-8)+(-8)+24$ b. $-10-(-10)$

c. $36+(-6)\cdot 5$ d. $10(2)-(-2)(10)$

e. $3+(-2)(3)-3$ f. $98+(-2)(10)-9(5)$

6.2.4 What if they are greater than one?

Multiplying Mixed Numbers

In the past few lessons, you have worked to develop a strong understanding of multiplying fractions. Can this understanding help you to multiply numbers that are greater than one but not whole numbers? In this and the next lessons, you will investigate this question.

6-70. Mrs. McElveen plans to devote a $1\frac{1}{2}$-meter by $1\frac{1}{2}$-meter section of the school garden to tomato plants. She is wondering how much area would be devoted to tomatoes. Owen made the sketch below right to help determine the area. With your team, answer the following questions.

a. Explain how this sketch shows a $1\frac{1}{2}$-meter by $1\frac{1}{2}$-meter area.

b. Copy and complete the generic rectangle at right.

c. How much area in the school garden is devoted to the tomato plants?

6-71. In the previous problem, you multiplied two mixed numbers using a generic rectangle. For each of the generic rectangles below,

- Write the two numbers that are being multiplied, that is, the length and width of the rectangle.

- *Predict* the approximate size of the product and be ready to **explain** your thinking.

- Copy the rectangle onto your paper and use it to multiply the given numbers.

- Write each answer as a complete multiplication sentence. (An example of a multiplication sentence from problem 6-70 would be $1\frac{1}{2} \cdot 1\frac{1}{2} = 1 + \frac{1}{2} + \frac{1}{2} + \frac{1}{4} = 2\frac{1}{4}$.)

- **Compare** the exact answer with your prediction. How close did you get?

Problem continues on next page →

6-71.   *Problem continued from previous page.*

a.

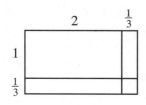

b.

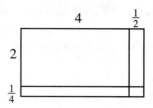

c.

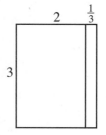

d.

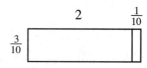

6-72.   Jules is a champion long-distance runner. He has measured the length of his route through a park and found that it is $4\frac{3}{5}$ of a mile long. Today he ran his route $2\frac{2}{3}$ times before he had to stop to rest. He wants to know how many miles he ran.

a.   Without calculating, predict approximately how far you think Jules has run. **Explain** your estimation strategy to your teammates.

b.   Draw a generic rectangle to help Jules figure out $2\frac{2}{3}\cdot 4\frac{3}{5}$.

c.   Jules is not satisfied with the answer, because he cannot tell how many miles he has run. Work with your team to estimate the size of each part of the generic rectangle and tell Jules about how far he has run.

Making Connections: Course 1

6-73.   When making estimates, it is sometimes useful to approximate unfamiliar fractions by **comparing** them to numbers that you are more familiar with.

Work with your team to determine which fractions from the list given below satisfy each of the conditions in parts (a) through (d). Be prepared to **explain** your ideas.

$$\frac{1}{12}, \frac{7}{6}, \frac{13}{12}, \frac{15}{9}, \frac{6}{100}, \frac{6}{7}, \frac{30}{16}, \frac{2}{17}, \frac{12}{25}, \frac{2}{20}, \frac{98}{100}, \frac{6}{11}, \frac{6}{5}, \frac{4}{2}, \frac{20}{11}$$

a.   Which of these fractions are greater than or equal to $1\frac{1}{2}$?

b.   Which of these fractions are close to the number 1?

c.   Which of these fractions are close to $\frac{1}{2}$?

d.   Which of these numbers are close to 0?

e.   Work with your team to use these numbers to label each dot on the number line shown below.

6-74.   Complete each of the fractions shown below to satisfy the given conditions.

a.   Make each of these fractions close, but not equal, to 0: $\frac{\square}{16}, \frac{\square}{10}, \frac{4}{\square}, \frac{10}{\square}$

b.   Make each of these fractions close, but not equal, to $\frac{1}{2}$: $\frac{\square}{15}, \frac{\square}{9}, \frac{4}{\square}, \frac{10}{\square}$

c.   Make each of these fractions greater than 1 but less than 2: $\frac{6}{\square}, \frac{10}{\square}, \frac{\square}{6}, \frac{\square}{3}$

6-75.   GENERIC-RECTANGLE CHALLENGE

Complete the diagram at right and write the corresponding multiplication sentence.

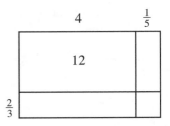

METHODS AND MEANINGS

Multiplying Fractions

You can find the product of two fractions, such as $\frac{2}{3}$ and $\frac{3}{4}$, by multiplying the numerators (tops) of the fractions together and dividing that by the product of the denominators (bottoms). So $\frac{2}{3} \cdot \frac{3}{4} = \frac{6}{12}$, which is equivalent to $\frac{1}{2}$. Similarly, $\frac{4}{7} \cdot \frac{3}{5} = \frac{12}{35}$. If we write this in algebraic terms, we would say $\frac{a}{b} \cdot \frac{c}{d} = \frac{a \cdot c}{b \cdot d}$.

The reason that this rule works can be seen using an area model of multiplication, as shown at right. The product of the denominators is the total number of smaller rectangles, while the product of the numerators is the number of the rectangles that are double shaded.

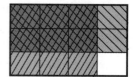

6-76.   Billy and Ken, the school cross-country stars, were each running at cross-country practice. Billy was going to run $\frac{3}{4}$ of the training course and Ken was going to run $\frac{1}{2}$ of the course. However, during practice it started raining and they could not finish their runs. Billy had finished $\frac{1}{3}$ of his run, while Ken had finished $\frac{1}{2}$ of his run. Draw a picture to determine which cross-country star ran the farthest.

6-77.   Convert each mixed number to a fraction greater than one, or each fraction greater than one to a mixed number.

a. $5\frac{3}{11}$ b. $\frac{49}{4}$ c. $3\frac{1}{20}$ d. $\frac{603}{100}$

6-78.   Without writing anything down, subtract $275 - 47$. **Explain** your strategy in words.

6-79.   Represent each of the following numbers two ways: by drawing an area model and using a number line.

   a. $1\frac{2}{3}$

   b.   125%

6-80.   On your own grid paper, draw a rectangle with a width of 6 cm and a height of 8 cm.

   a.   Draw a similar rectangle that is enlarged 300%.

   b.   Draw a similar rectangle with lengths that are $\frac{2}{3}$ of the original lengths.

6.2.5 How can I get an answer that is one number?

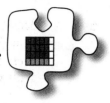

Multiplying with Mixed Numbers and Fractions Greater Than One

In Lesson 6.2.4, you learned a method for multiplying mixed numbers. While useful, this method does not easily result in an answer that has a very clear size. In some problems, it is important to know an exact answer and to be able to express that answer as one number. In this lesson, you will develop a strategy for multiplying fractions greater than one that will result in a one-number answer.

6-81. Each batch of Anita's famous bran muffins calls for $3\frac{1}{3}$ cups of bran. Anita wants to make $2\frac{3}{4}$ batches of muffins, so she has enough for everyone in her class. She started her calculations by writing $2\frac{3}{4} \cdot 3\frac{1}{3}$ and drawing a generic rectangle.

a. Work with your team to draw a generic rectangle to help Anita figure out how much bran she needs.

b. Anita is not satisfied. *"Wait,"* she says, *"I can't tell how much bran to buy. There has to be a way to get an answer that is one number."* Discuss this with your team. Is there a way that you could get an answer that is one number? Be ready to share your ideas with the class.

c. Write $2\frac{3}{4}$ and $3\frac{1}{3}$ as fractions greater than one. Does this make it easier to multiply and get a single number answer? Why or why not? Is your answer easy to place on a number line?

Discussion Points

How can we change the form of each number
so that we can apply the same strategy?

How can we tell how big this product is?

6-82. How can Anita tell how much bran to buy? Work with your team to find a strategy to place Anita's product on a number line.

Making Connections: Course 1

6-83.   Jessica was working on multiplying $4\frac{2}{5} \cdot 3\frac{1}{3}$, when she thought
of a shortcut. *"Wait,"* she said, *"Can't we just multiply* $4 \cdot 3$ *and
then* $\frac{2}{5} \cdot \frac{1}{3}$ *and then add the results?"* Consider Jessica's idea
with your team as you answer the questions below.

   a.   What result would you get using Jessica's method?
Is this result correct?

   b.   Work with your team to **explain** to Jessica what she is missing.

6-84.   For each of the following products,
   • Work with your team to estimate the size of the product. Be sure to **explain**
your thinking.
   • Use the method you developed in problem 6-81 to find the exact product.
   • Place the product on a number line.

   a. $2\frac{2}{3} \cdot \frac{1}{8}$ b. $4\frac{4}{5} \cdot 1\frac{2}{3}$ c. $\frac{4}{7} \cdot 2\frac{1}{2}$

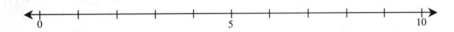

6-85.   LEARNING LOG

In your Learning Log, explain how you can multiply mixed
numbers and fractions greater than one. Be sure to include
examples to demonstrate your thinking. Title this entry
"Multiplying Mixed Numbers and Fractions Greater than
One" and label it with today's date.

6-86.   Jill lives $3\frac{1}{2}$ miles from school. One morning, her friend was giving her a ride.
When they were $\frac{2}{3}$ of the way to school, their car broke down and they had to
walk the rest of the way. Draw a picture to help you figure out how far they
walked.

6-87.   For each of the following products, estimate approximately how big the answer
should be. **Explain** your reasoning. Then multiply each set of numbers to see
how close you got.

   a. $2\frac{1}{3} \cdot 1\frac{1}{2}$ b. $5\frac{2}{5} \cdot 2\frac{3}{4}$ c. $3\frac{1}{10} \cdot 2\frac{7}{10}$

6-88.   Complete the web at right to
         represent 0.33 as a percent, a fraction,
         and with a description.

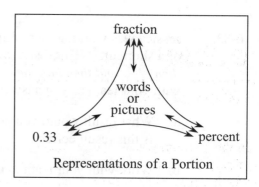

6-89.   Draw a rectangle. Label the lengths
         of the sides. Enlarge it so that the
         ratio of sides of your new rectangle to
         the original one is $\frac{5}{2}$. What are the
         new dimensions?

6-90.   Copy the axes below and complete the scales.

a.

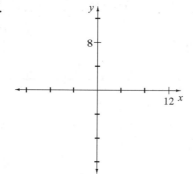

b.

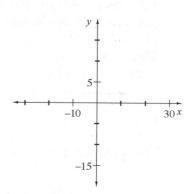

6.2.6 What if they are not fractions?

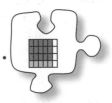

Multiplying Decimals and Percents

In this section, you will apply the understanding that you have developed for finding parts of parts to multiplying decimals. As you work with your team, you will be thinking about whether particular answers make sense, relying on your understanding of the relative size of a part of a part.

6-91. At the beginning of class, Lorna turned to her team and said, *"Wow, you guys! We have got to go shopping at Daisy's tomorrow! Sunglasses are on sale for 70% off, and I have a coupon for 40% off! That makes 110% off, so the store will have to pay me! How cool is that?"*

"No way!" Mandy said. *"If sunglasses are 70% off, that means you only have to pay 30% of the original price, right? If you have a 40% off coupon, then you pay 60% of the price. 30% and 60% is 90%, so you would actually have to pay 90% of the regular price. Oops, this means that the coupon makes you pay more! That doesn't make sense!"*

Tony suggested that they figure out how to use what they have been learning about finding parts of parts to represent 60% (the percent they have to pay if they are using a 40% off coupon) of 30% (the percent of the price of the sunglasses remaining after the 70% discount).

Your task: With your team,

- Work with your team to make sense of what Lorna, Mandy, and Tony each think about this situation.

- Find at least **three ways** to represent 60% of 30% using diagrams or numbers.

- Use your representations to **make sense** of the problem and figure out if the sunglasses are free.

- If they are not free, help Lorna figure out what portion of the original price she would have to pay.

- Be prepared to **explain** your ideas to the class.

6-92.   Thinking about multiple representations of portions can help us make sense of multiplying percents and decimals. Consider this as you answer the questions below.

a.   If you have not done so already, represent 60% of 30% using decimals and write the result of calculating 60% of 30% as a decimal.

b.   Chika thinks that $0.4(0.2) = 0.8$. Is she correct? Work with your team to find a way to show whether Chika's answer makes sense. (You do not need to calculate the correct answer yet.)

c.   What happens when you multiply one-tenth by one-tenth? Use fraction multiplication to find the answer, and then represent the problem and answer using decimals.

d.   Multiply $\frac{1}{10} \cdot \frac{4}{100}$. Then represent this problem and answer using decimals.

e.   Calculate Chika's product from part (b). That is, multiply $0.4(0.2)$.

6-93.   Ben and Connor needed to calculate 20% of 4.31. They started by drawing the generic rectangle at right.

$\frac{2}{10}$

a.   Why did they write $\frac{2}{10}$?

b.   Copy their generic rectangle onto your own paper and work with your team to label the missing dimensions and find the product.

c.   Ben wrote the work shown at right. Work with your team to **explain** how his work is related to the work you did with the generic rectangle in part (a).

$$\begin{array}{r} 4.31 \\ \times\ 0.2 \\ \hline 0.002 \\ 0.06 \\ +\ 0.8 \\ \hline \end{array}$$

d.   Help Ben complete his work by writing the answer to his multiplication problem.

e.   Why did Ben line up the decimals points in his method, instead of writing them sum as shown at right?

$$\begin{array}{r} 0.002 \\ 0.06 \\ +\ \ 0.8 \\ \hline \end{array}$$

6-94.   Work with your team to **make sense** of another method for multiplying
         0.2(4.31).

    a.   Write 0.2(4.31) as a product of fractions and then multiply.

    b.   Connor has shown the work at right. How does the work you
         did with fractions in part (a) help **explain** where he has
         decided to place the decimal point in his answer? Discuss this
         with your team and be prepared to share your ideas with the
         class.

6-95.   Mohamed is multiplying 3.9(0.6). His work is shown at right.

    a.   Work with your team to figure out where the numbers 0.54
         and 1.8 come from in Mohamed's work and whether he is
         correct.

    b.   Will the answer be more than 2 or less than 2? **Explain** how you know.

    c.   Mohamed notices that to get the answer, he will add 5-tenths and 8-tenths.
         How should he write that sum in his work?

    d.   Finish Mohamed's work to find the product 3.9(0.6).

6-96.   Without a calculator, find each of the following products.

    a.   0.3(0.01)   b.   1.4(0.2)   c.   2.8(0.9)

6-97.   Jack designed a bridge that will be 0.2 miles long and $\frac{3}{5}$ of the bridge has been
         built. How long is the section of the bridge that is finished? Show how you
         know.

6-98.   Brianna thinks that $3\% \cdot 4\% = 12\%$, but Caitlin is not so sure. What do you
         think? **Explain** your answer.

MATH NOTES

METHODS AND **M**EANINGS

Multiplying Mixed Numbers

An efficient method for multiplying mixed numbers is to convert them to fractions greater than one, find the product as you would with fractions less than one, and then convert them back to a mixed number, if necessary. Here are three examples.

$$1\frac{2}{3} \cdot 2\frac{3}{4} = \frac{5}{3} \cdot \frac{11}{4} = \frac{55}{12} = 4\frac{7}{12} \qquad\qquad 1\frac{3}{5} \cdot \frac{2}{9} = \frac{8}{5} \cdot \frac{2}{9} = \frac{16}{45}$$

$$2\frac{1}{3} \cdot 4\frac{1}{2} = \frac{7}{3} \cdot \frac{9}{2} = \frac{63}{6} = 10\frac{3}{6} = 10\frac{1}{2}$$

Review & Preview

6-99.   Draw a number line from 0 to 2 like the example shown below. Then write the following numbers in their correct place on the number line.

$$0.2 \qquad \frac{13}{26} \qquad 1.5 \qquad \frac{1}{8} \qquad 1.9 \qquad \frac{7}{8} \qquad 1.09 \qquad \frac{3}{5} \qquad 1.19$$

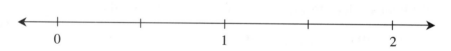

6-100.   Melissa wants to re-sod her yard. Her backyard has a rectangular lawn area that is $24\frac{1}{2}$ feet by 18 feet. Her front yard has two rectangular areas, one of which measures $18\frac{1}{2}$ feet by $14\frac{1}{2}$ feet. The other measures $12\frac{1}{2}$ feet by $14\frac{1}{2}$ feet. How many square feet of sod does Melissa need? Show all of your work clearly.

6-101.   Mrs. Ferguson, your school librarian, asks you
to conduct a survey of how many books
students read during the year. You get the
following results: 12, 24, 10, 36, 12, 21, 35,
10, 8, 12, 15, 20, 18, 25, 21, and 9.

a.   Use the data to create a stem-and-leaf plot.

b.   Calculate the mean, median, and mode for
the data.

6-102.   Simplify each expression below.

a. $8 + (-6) + 4$ b. $-15 + 3 + 6$ c. $-8 + 12 + 2$ d. $6(-8)$

e. $5(-9)$ f. $-61 + (-13)$ g. $4(-7)$ h. $120 + (-15)$

6-103.   Without a calculator, simplify the following decimal expressions.

a. $0.04(0.7)$ b. $7.142 + 0.9$ c. $(1.8)(0.3)$

6.2.7 How will multiplying change my number?

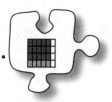

Multiplication Number Sense

What if you wanted to enlarge the dragon mascot from Lesson 6.1.1 to make it big enough to fit on the side of a warehouse? What if you wanted to make it a little bit smaller so that it would fit on a postcard, for example? What number could you multiply each side of the mascot by to accomplish these tasks? In this lesson, you will investigate the effect on a quantity of multiplying it by different numbers.

6-104.   HOW MANY TIMES?

Shane loves his job as treasurer of "ACT NOW," the performing arts club at Hollygood High. He worked hard to write out a budget for the upcoming trip to New York City and was excited when the principal returned it to him with the following note. *"Good job, Shane. Your budget has been approved with only one change: please multiply all expenditure amounts by $\frac{5}{6}$."*

When Shane reported this news to Tammy, the club president, she was ecstatic. *"That's fantastic!"* she said, *"I thought our budget would be cut, not multiplied. Now maybe we can visit Rockefeller Center too."*

"Actually," Shane replied, *"I'm afraid we are going to have to skip a few activities."*

Has the club just received good news or bad? With your team, decide whether the principal's memo means the club can spend more or less money than Shane had thought. Be ready to **explain** your ideas to the class.

6-105.   Shane has just become editor for his school newspaper. He is working on reducing and enlarging photos for a page of advertising and needs your help. He knows that he must multiply each side length by the same number in order for the photographs to look right, but he is having trouble figuring out what number to choose for different layouts.

Your task: Get a copy of the Lesson 6.2.7 Resource Page from your teacher. Work with your team to figure by out what number Shane must multiply each side length of his original 3×5 photo to enlarge or reduce it to each of the other indicated sizes.

6-106.   Copy the number line shown below onto your own paper and mark the location
          of each of the multipliers (also called **scale factors**) from problem 6-105.
          Then answer the following questions. Be prepared to **explain** your ideas to
          the class.

          a.   Which of the scale factors enlarged the original photo the most? Which one
               reduced the photo the most? Which number had the least effect on the size
               of the photo?

          b.   Is there a relationship between the location of each number on the number
               line and the effect that multiplying the lengths by that number has on the
               size? **Explain**.

          c.   Which multiplier had the very least effect on the size of the photo?
               Explain why this makes sense.

6-107.   The student portraits have arrived! Each photo measures 2 by 3 inches and
          Shane needs to lay out a page that requires him to enlarge and reduce them in
          many ways. **Explain** which of the numbers listed below Shane should multiply
          each side length by to achieve each of the desired results. **Explain** your
          reasoning in each case.

$$\frac{10}{10}, \frac{8}{7}, \frac{8}{9}, \frac{1}{10}, \frac{8}{8}, \frac{10}{3}$$

          a.   To make the photo much bigger.

          b.   To make the photo a little bigger.

          c.   To make the photo much smaller.

          d.   To make the photo a little smaller.

          e.   To keep the photo the same size.

6-108.   The publishing deadline was approaching and Shane and Tammy were arguing
          about scale factors. Shane thought that to enlarge the 3 by 5 photo to a 6 by 10,
          they should multiply by $\frac{6}{3}$. Tammy was sure that they should multiply by $\frac{10}{5}$.
          Justin said it would be much simpler to just multiply each side by 2. Which
          student's method will work? **Explain** how you know.

6-109.   Stop the presses! Shane has just realized that he needs to enlarge his 3 by 5 photo to be a different size. He needs to make the photo fit onto a large poster. The smaller dimension, 3 inches, needs to be enlarged to 8 inches. What should Shane multiply each side length by to enlarge the photo?

6-110.   The multipliers that you found in problem 6-105 can be written as fractions, decimals, or percents, and some as whole numbers. Write each multiplier in as many forms as you can find.

6-111.   LEARNING LOG

Work with your team to discuss each of the following questions. Then write your ideas as a Learning Log entry. Title this entry "Multiplication Number Sense" and label it with today's date.

What kinds of numbers would I multiply by to get answers
that are just a little bigger than my starting number?
A lot bigger?

What kinds of numbers would I multiply by to get answers
that are just a little smaller than my starting number?
A lot smaller?

METHODS AND MEANINGS

Multiplying Decimals

There are at least two ways to multiply decimals. One way is to convert the decimals to fractions and use your knowledge of fraction multiplication to compute the answer. The other way is to use the method that you have used to multiply integers; the only difference is that you need to keep track of where the decimal point is as you record each line.

Here we show how to compute 1.4(2.35) both ways by using generic rectangles.

	2	$\frac{3}{10}$	$\frac{5}{100}$
1	2	$\frac{3}{10}$	$\frac{5}{100}$
$\frac{4}{10}$	$\frac{8}{10}$	$\frac{12}{100}$	$\frac{20}{1000}$

	2	0.3	0.05
1	2	0.3	0.05
0.4	0.8	0.12	0.020

If you carried out the computation as above, you can calculate the product in either of these two ways. In the first one, we write down all of the values in the smaller rectangles within the generic rectangle and add the six numbers. In the second example, we combine the values in each row and then add the two rows. The answer is 3.29 since there are zero thousandths in the product.

$$
\begin{array}{r}
2.35 \\
\underline{1.4} \\
0.020 \\
0.12 \\
0.8 \\
0.05 \\
0.3 \\
\underline{2.0} \\
3.290
\end{array}
$$

$$
\begin{array}{r}
2.35 \\
\underline{1.4} \\
0.940 \\
\underline{2.35} \\
3.29
\end{array}
$$

6-112.   Copy and complete each of the Diamond Problems below.
          The pattern used in the Diamond Problems is shown at right.

a.   b.   c.

6-113.   Multiply the following fractions.

          a. $\frac{7}{8} \cdot \frac{5}{6}$ b. $\frac{2}{13} \cdot \frac{4}{5}$ c. $\frac{6}{7} \cdot \frac{6}{7}$ d. $\frac{4}{7} \cdot \frac{3}{8}$

6-114.   Find the area of the figure at right. All angles are right
          angles. Show your work.

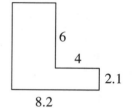

6-115.   Steve shuffles a standard deck of 52 playing cards and
          starts to turn them over one at a time. The first three
          cards he turns over are an ace, a four, and a jack.

          a. How many cards are left in the deck?

          b. How many of the remaining cards are aces?

          c. What is the probability that the fourth card will be an ace?

          d. Instead of getting an ace, he gets a two as the fourth card. The fifth card is
              a five. What is the probability that the next card will be a king?

6-116.   Genevieve is an architect and she has just finished the plans for a new library!
          She built a scale model to take to a city planning meeting. The city council
          loves her design so much that they have asked her for two new ones. Help her
          decide how she will calculate the measurements of her new model to satisfy
          each of the given conditions.

          a. They want a model much smaller than her original model to fit in a display
              of the entire city.

          b. They want a model a little bit larger than the one she built to sit on a
              pedestal at the entrance of the old library building.

Making Connections: Course 1

6.3.1 Are they the same?

Equivalent Fractions and Ratios

In the previous section, you learned how to multiply fractions and what kinds of multipliers make a product larger, smaller, or the same as the starting value. In Section 6.1, you learned how to enlarge and reduce shapes and how to write and use ratios that **compare** two quantities. In this lesson, these ideas will come together as you learn about and name a powerful tool for finding equivalent ratios and fractions. The concept that you will investigate in this lesson is one that you will use many times throughout your mathematics career!

6-117.   Ms. Vazquez had a reputation for telling math jokes. She started class today with this one:

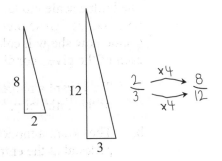

> Ron was picking up his pizza at the takeout window. The clerk asked him, *"Do you want your pizza cut into 8 slices or 12?"*
>
> *"Better cut it into 8 slices,"* Ron replied. *"I'm not hungry enough to eat 12."*

Some students thought the joke was funny. Do you? What is the fraction concept that makes the joke work?

6-118.   Emon and his team were working on the following problem.
A right triangle with a height of 8 units and a base of 2 units has been enlarged. The new height is 12 units and the new base is 3 units. Was the enlargement done correctly? How can you be sure?"

Emon thought. *"I'll write two ratios, one that **compares** the bases and one that **compares** the heights of the two triangles. If the ratios are equivalent, then the enlargement must have been done correctly. If the ratios are different, then it must have been done incorrectly."*
His work is shown at the right.

Problem continues on next page →

6-118.   *Problem continued from previous page.*

"*Wait,*" he told his team, "*This reminds me of something we did when we were multiplying fractions.*"

He drew the diagram at right and showed it to his team.

$$\frac{2}{3} \cdot \frac{4}{4} = \frac{2 \cdot 4}{3 \cdot 4} = \frac{8}{12}$$

a. What is the connection that Emon is making between equivalent ratios and fraction multiplication? Work with your team to **make sense** of what Emon is showing in his diagrams.

b. Was the triangle enlargement done correctly? How can you be sure?

6-119.   ONE-DERFUL ONE

While working on problem 6-118, Emon's team member, Wanda, noticed a very useful connection. She recognized that *any* fraction in which the numerator and denominator are the same is equivalent to 1, and that multiplying a number by 1 leaves that number unchanged. "*WOW,*" she said, "*I can use this idea to find a whole bunch of equivalent fractions and ratios!*" She showed her team the work at right. "*Look!*" she said, "*It's the same as using a GIANT ONE!*"

$$\frac{3}{5} \cdot \frac{2}{2} = \frac{6}{10}$$

a. Discuss Wanda's work with your team. Does it **make sense**? Is $\frac{3}{5}$ equivalent to $\frac{6}{10}$? How can you be sure?

b. Find at least two other fractions or ratios that are equivalent to $\frac{3}{5}$.

6-120.   Use the idea of the Giant One to find at least four fractions or ratios that are equivalent to each of the following:

a. $\frac{7}{11}$ b. 1 to 8   c. $\frac{9}{8}$

6-121.   LEARNING LOG

Write a Learning Log entry to summarize what you learned today about the Giant One and its uses. Include examples of how the Giant One is used. Title this entry "The Giant One and Equivalent Fractions" and label it with today's date.

6-122.   Simplify each of the following expressions.

   a. $(4+8) \div 12 + 23$ b. $3 \cdot (8-5) + 6 + 2 \cdot 7$

   c. $49 \div 7 \cdot 5 + 4 \cdot (3+2)$

6-123.   Mrs. Olson has to find the class average for the last test. She also needs to give
           the school principal information about how well the class is doing. The test
           scores were 99, 92, 45, 90, 65, 54, 68, 75, 77, 86, 85, 72, 38, 85, 91, 85, 10, 70,
           65, and 73.

   a.   Make a stem-and-leaf plot of the test scores.

   b.   Find the mean, median, and mode of the scores.

   c.   Which measure do you think most fairly represents how well the class is
        doing? **Explain**.

6-124.   Convert each mixed number to a fraction greater than one, or each fraction
           greater than one to a mixed number.

   a. $4\frac{1}{8}$ b. $\frac{302}{3}$ c. $100\frac{2}{5}$ d. $\frac{18}{3}$

6-125.   Maciel and Alejandro were trying to figure out the answer to $8.42 + 0.3$. Maciel
           thinks the answer is 8.72, but Alejandro got 8.45. Who is correct? Why? What
           did the other person do wrong?

6-126.   On graph paper, plot the points (2, 3), (4, 7), and (8, 7).

   a.   Name one more point that could be plotted so that the four points create a
        parallelogram.

   b.   Name a point that could be plotted with the original three points to create a
        trapezoid.

6.3.2 How can I use it?

Using the Multiplicative Identity

In the previous lesson, you learned about a powerful new tool for finding equivalent ratios and fractions – the Giant One. This way of thinking about equivalence can be applied to different situations and problem contexts. Today you and your team will expand your understanding of the Giant One. You will see how it can be used to solve problems as well as to investigate new applications.

6-127.   SO MANY CHOICES

Bertrand was feeling confused. *"There are so many ways to write the Giant One! How do I know which one to use?"* he lamented. How can Bertrand decide which Giant One to use? Work with your team to answer the following questions and come up with a strategy.

a.   Find the correct numerators for the Giant Ones below.

   i. $\frac{3}{4} \cdot \boxed{} = \frac{}{20}$ *ii.* $\frac{3}{4} \cdot \boxed{} = \frac{}{44}$ *iii.* $\frac{3}{4} \cdot \boxed{} = \frac{}{100}$

   What computation could help you find the numbers to use in the Giant Ones?

b.   Find the missing numbers in parts (*i*) and (*ii*) below. Be ready to **explain** your strategies.

   i. $\frac{7}{12} \cdot \boxed{} = \frac{}{60}$ *ii.* $\frac{18}{72} \cdot \boxed{} = \frac{3}{}$

6-128.   Use what you have discovered about finding the necessary Giant Ones to complete the following problem.

$$\frac{35}{50} \cdot \boxed{} = \frac{}{10}$$

a.   How is the Giant One that you used here different from the ones than you found in problem 6-127? Does a Giant One always have to be created with two whole numbers?

b.   Can you think of a different way to **make sense** of this problem?

6-129.   How could you use the idea of the Giant One to help you convert fractions to percents? Discuss this with your team and then use your ideas to convert each of the following fractions to percents.

a. $\frac{3}{5}$ b. $\frac{5}{8}$ c. $\frac{649}{1000}$ d. $\frac{705}{500}$

6-130.   Sometimes it is useful to express a fraction in **lowest terms**, or using the smallest whole numbers possible to express the fraction. For example, $\frac{60}{70}$, $\frac{30}{35}$, and $\frac{6}{7}$ are equivalent fractions, but the fraction $\frac{6}{7}$ is expressed in lowest terms. **Simplifying** a fraction is the process of rewriting it in lowest terms.

With your team, consider how the Giant One could help you simplify fractions as you answer the questions below.

a.   Tessa has written the work shown at right. Copy her work on your own paper and show the giant one and each of the two equivalent fractions.

$$\frac{55}{500} = \frac{5 \cdot 11}{5 \cdot 100} = \frac{11}{100}$$

b.   Does Tessa's work make sense? Is $\frac{11}{100}$ expressed in lowest terms? How can you tell? Be prepared to **explain** your ideas to the class.

c.   Tessa is doing well! She decided to try another problem and wrote the work shown at right. Is her work correct? Is her fraction expressed in lowest terms? If so, explain how you can tell. If not, help her figure out the lowest terms for this fraction.

$$\frac{28}{60} = \frac{2 \cdot 14}{2 \cdot 30} = \frac{14}{30}$$

d.   Work with your team to simplify each of the following fractions into their lowest terms.

i. $\frac{24}{36}$ ii. $\frac{30}{48}$ iii. $\frac{56}{98}$

6-131.   LEARNING LOG

Write a Learning Log entry to summarize what you learned today about some of the uses of the Giant One. Include examples of how the Giant One is used to convert fractions to percents and to simplify fractions. Title this entry "Applications of the Giant One" and label it with today's date.

METHODS AND **M**EANINGS

MATH NOTES

Multiplicative Identity

If any number or expression is multiplied by the number one, the number or expression does not change. The number one is called the **multiplicative identity**. Formally this is written:

$$1 \cdot x = x \cdot 1 = x \text{ for all values of } x.$$

One way the multiplicative identity is used is to create equivalent fractions using a Giant One.

$$\frac{2}{3} \cdot \frac{2}{2} = \frac{4}{6}$$

Multiplying a fraction by a fraction equivalent to one creates a new, equivalent fraction.

6-132.   Victor and Hugo were shooting baskets. Hugo made 6 of his 10 shots. Victor made 10 out of his 15 shots. Who is the better shooter? Show all of your work or **explain** your reasoning clearly.

6-133.   Without a calculator, find the following products:

a. $\frac{11}{4}$ of $\frac{3}{7}$ b. $\frac{5}{12} \cdot 2$ c. $4.16(0.2)$ d. $4\frac{2}{5} \cdot 1\frac{1}{3}$

6-134.   Copy the dot pattern below and draw Figures 0, 4, and 5. **Explain** how you could know the number of dots in any figure if you knew the figure number.

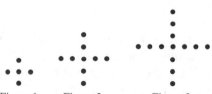

Figure 1   Figure 2   Figure 3

6-135. Copy and complete each of the following Giant One problems.

a. $\frac{5}{3} \cdot$ 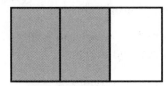 $= \frac{}{18}$

b. $\frac{28}{63} =$ 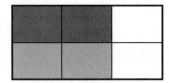 $\cdot \frac{}{4}$

c. $\frac{9}{20} \cdot$ $= \frac{}{100}$

6-136. Each of the following pairs of diagrams shows a first and second step that could be used to represent a multiplication problem. For each pair, write a multiplication problem and its solution.

a.

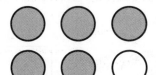

b.

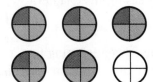

Chapter 6 Closure   What have I learned?

Reflection and Synthesis

The activities below offer you a chance to reflect on what you have learned during this chapter. As you work, look for concepts that you feel very comfortable with, ideas that you would like to learn more about, and topics, you need more help with. Look for **connections** between ideas as well as **connections** with material you learned previously.

①   SUMMARIZING MY UNDERSTANDING

This section gives you an opportunity to show what you know about the main math ideas in this chapter.

Magic Book

You have been learning how to enlarge and reduce figures while maintaining their shape. You also learned about using ratios to **describe** relationships between shapes that differ in size. Finally, you learned to multiply fractions and find equivalent fractions. This section gives you an opportunity to showcase what you know about these concepts. Your teacher will provide you with instructions for how to create a "magic book." In this book, you will summarize your understanding of ratios and multiplication of fractions as well as show how your understanding can be used to solve problems.

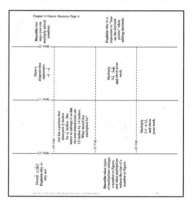

Assemble the Book: Follow your teacher's instructions to create a special book. It will become clear later why this is called a "magic book."

Review the Concepts: Use your Toolkit, textbook, and other classroom resources to review the main ideas from this chapter. Be able to explain what you know about ratios and how to use them to solve problems. Also, be able to multiply fractions and find equivalent fractions.

Examples to Show What You Know: Follow your teacher's instructions to reveal the hidden portion of the book. In this region of the book, show what you have learned about ratios, multiplying fractions, and equivalence.

②   ASSESSING MY UNDERSTANDING

Working the problems in this section will help you to evaluate which types of problems you feel comfortable with and which you need more help with.

Solve each problem as completely as you can. The table at the end of this closure section provides answers to these problems. It also tells you where you can find additional help and practice on problems like these.

CL 6-137. Draw a right triangle on grid paper that has a base of 4 units and a height of 2 units. Enlarge it so that each side is 2.5 times as long as the original.

CL 6-138. Which portion in each pair is greater? **Explain** how you know.

     a.   0.1 and 0.01   b. $\frac{8}{10}$ and 0.91

CL 6-139. Simplify the following expressions without a calculator.

     a. $5(2 \cdot 3 + 1) + 4(-6)$ b. $10 \cdot \frac{3}{8}$

     c. $4.9(0.2)$ d. $7.15 + 0.8$

CL 6-140. For each of the following products, estimate approximately how big the answer should be. **Explain** your reasoning. Then multiply each set of numbers to see how close you got.

     a. $1\frac{1}{10} \cdot 2\frac{3}{10}$ b. $4\frac{2}{3} \cdot 3$

CL 6-141. Find three fractions that are equivalent to each of the following fractions.

     a. $\frac{4}{7}$ b. $\frac{1}{3}$

CL 6-142. **Describe** how each of the following multipliers would change the size of a photograph.

     a. $\frac{15}{2}$ b. $\frac{4}{3}$ c. $\frac{5}{6}$ d. $\frac{12}{12}$

CL 6-143. The video club at Tolt Jr. High does a live broadcast at school every morning, covering school news, general announcements, sports, and the weather. The morning weather report predicts a 10% chance of snow today.

    a.   The kids listening to the broadcast went crazy! Many started planning snow activities for after school. Should the kids be this excited? **Explain**.

    b.   Write this probability as a fraction. Now write three more fractions that are equivalent to 10%.

    c.   Write the probability of snow as a decimal. Copy the probability number line shown below and place the decimal. **Explain** what the 0 and 1 mean regarding today's weather report.

CL 6-144. Write $\frac{17}{5}$ as a mixed number. Then make up any mixed number and show how you can write it as a fraction greater than one.

CL 6-145. For each of the problems above, do the following:

- Draw a bar or number line that represents 0 to 10.

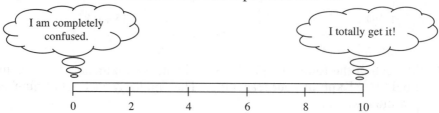

- Color or shade in a portion of the bar that represents your level of understanding and comfort with completing that problem on your own.

If any of your bars are less than a 5, choose *one* of those problems and do one of the following tasks:

- Write two questions that you would like to ask about that problem.

- Brainstorm two things that you DO know about that type of problem.

If all of your bars are at 5 or above, choose one problem and do one of these tasks:

- Write two questions you might ask or hints you might give to a student that was stuck on the problem.

- Make a new problem that is similar and more challenging than that problem and solve it.

③　　　SUPPORTING MY UNDERSTANDING

You have several tools and references available to help support your learning – your teacher, your study team, your math book, and your Toolkit to name only a few. At the end of each chapter you will have an opportunity to review your Toolkit for completeness as well as to revise or update your Toolkit to better reflect your current understanding of big ideas.

The main elements of your Toolkit should be your Learning Log, Math Notes and the vocabulary used in this chapter. Math words that are new to this chapter appear in bold in the text. Refer to the lists provided below and follow your teacher's instructions to revise your Toolkit, which will help make it a useful reference for you as you complete this chapter and prepare to begin the next one.

Learning Log Entries

- Lesson 6.1.2 – Enlarging Figures
- Lesson 6.1.3 – Ratios
- Lesson 6.2.3 – Multiplying Fractions
- Lesson 6.2.5 – Multiplying Mixed Numbers and Fractions Greater than One
- Lesson 6.2.7 – Multiplication Number Sense
- Lesson 6.3.1 – The Giant One and Equivalent Fractions
- Lesson 6.3.2 – Applications of the Giant One

Math Notes

- Lesson 6.1.4 – Ratios
- Lesson 6.2.2 – Mixed Numbers and Fractions Greater than One
- Lesson 6.2.4 – Multiplying Fractions
- Lesson 6.2.6 – Multiplying Mixed Numbers
- Lesson 2.2.7 – Multiplying Decimals
- Lesson 6.3.2 – Multiplicative Identity

Mathematical Vocabulary

The following is a list of vocabulary found in this chapter. Some of the words have been seen in the previous chapter. The words in bold are the words new to this chapter. Make sure that you are familiar with the terms below and know what they mean. For the words you do not know, refer to the glossary or index. You might also add these words to your Toolkit so that you can reference them in the future.

area	dimensions	**enlarge**
equivalent fractions	**equivalent ratios**	generic rectangle
lowest terms	**mixed number**	**multiplicative**
identity	product	**ratio**
reduce	**scale factor**	

Process Words

compare	create	describe
enlarge	estimate	explain
make sense	reduce	represent
simplify	visualize	

Making Connections: Course 1

Answers and Support for Closure Activity #2
Assessing My Understanding

Problem	Solution	Need Help?	More Practice
CL 6-137.		Lessons 6.1.1, 6.1.2, 6.1.3, and 6.2.7 Math Notes box in Lesson 6.1.4 Learning Logs (problems 6-12 and 6-111)	Problems 6-10, 6-13, 6-19, 6-25, 6-80, and 6-118
CL 6-138.	a. $0.1 > 0.01$: this can be proven by converting the decimals into fractions with equal denominators, $0.1 = \frac{1}{10} = \frac{10}{100}$ and $0.01 = \frac{1}{100}$, $\frac{10}{100} > \frac{1}{100}$. b. $\frac{8}{10} < 0.91$: this can be proven by converting the numbers into fractions with equal denominators, $\frac{8}{10} = \frac{80}{100}$ and $0.91 = \frac{91}{100}$, $\frac{80}{100} < \frac{91}{100}$, or converting the fraction into a decimal, $\frac{8}{10} = 0.8$, $0.8 < 0.91$.	Lessons 6.1.3, 6.1.4, 6.2.6, and 6.3.1 Math Notes box in Lesson 6.3.2 Learning Logs (problems 6-24 and 6-121)	Problems 6-50, 6-68, 6-73, and 6-99
CL 6-139.	a. 11 b. $\frac{30}{8}$ or $3\frac{6}{8} = \frac{15}{4}$ or $3\frac{3}{4}$ c. 0.98 d. 7.95	Lessons 6.2.3, 6.2.5, and 6.2.6 Math Notes boxes in Lessons 6.2.4 and 6.2.7 Learning Logs (problems 6-64 and 6-85)	Problems 6-8, 6-15, 6-28, 6-69, and 6-96

Problem	Solution	Need Help?	More Practice
CL 6-140.	Estimations and reasoning vary. Sample solutions: a. $\frac{253}{100}$ or $2\frac{53}{100}$ b. 14	Lessons 6.2.2, 6.2.3, 6.2.4, 6.2.5, and 6.2.7 Math Notes boxes in Lessons 6.2.2, 6.2.4, and 6.2.6 Learning Logs (problems 6-85 and 6-111)	Problems 6-55, 6-60, 6-61, 6-71, 6-72, 6-84, and 6-87
CL 6-141.	Solutions will vary. Sample solutions: a. $\frac{8}{14}, \frac{12}{21}, \frac{40}{70}$ b. $\frac{2}{6}, \frac{3}{9}, \frac{10}{30}$	Lessons 6.3.1 and 6.3.2 Math Notes box in Lesson 6.3.2 Learning Logs (problems 6-121 and 6-131)	Problems 6-119 and 6-120
CL 6-142.	a. The measures of the sides of the photograph would all be increased by a factor of $\frac{15}{2}$. b. The measures of the sides of the photograph would all be increased by a factor of $\frac{4}{3}$. c. The measures of the sides of the photograph would all be decreased by a factor of $\frac{5}{6}$. d. The measures of the sides of the photograph would stay exactly the same as $\frac{12}{12} = 1$ and a factor of 1 neither increases or decreases a figure.	Lessons 6.1.1, 6.1.2, 6.1.3, 6.2.5, and 6.2.7 Math Notes box in Lesson 6.1.4 Learning Logs (problems 6-12, 6-24, 6-85, and 6-111)	Problems 6-3, 6-18, 6-19, 6-89, 6-106, 6-108, and 6-109

Problem		Solution	Need Help?	More Practice
CL 6-143.	a.	No, 10% is not a very good chance; it means that there is a 90% chance that it will not snow; 90% is significantly greater than 10%.	Lessons 6.1.4 and 6.3.2	Problems 6-33, 6-49, and 6-129
	b.	$\frac{1}{10}$; equivalent fraction examples will vary; sample examples: $\frac{2}{20}$, $\frac{3}{30}$, $\frac{10}{100}$.		
	c.	0 means that the event cannot/will not happen because it is impossible; 1 means that the event will certainly happen		

0.1
↓

```
┌─────────────┐
0             1
```

CL 6-144.	$3\frac{2}{5}$; examples will vary; sample examples: $4\frac{5}{6} = \frac{29}{6}$, $5\frac{7}{10} = \frac{57}{10}$, $7\frac{3}{4} = \frac{31}{4}$.	Lessons 6.2.2, 6.2.4, and 6.3.1 Math Notes box in Lesson 6.2.2 Learning Log (problem 6-121)	Problems 6-36, 6-47, 6-55, 6-66, 6-77, and 6-124

Right Prisms and Adding Portions

CHAPTER 7   Right Prisms and Adding Portions

You will begin this chapter by extending your thinking about measuring lengths and area to include measuring volume of three-dimensional objects.

In Section 7.2, you will find ways to divide different amounts of licorice among different numbers of people. You will then learn strategies to divide fractions into parts of the same size so that you can add them together. You will extend this thinking to include strategies for adding and subtraction fractions and decimals.

In Section 7.3, you will extend your understanding of adding and subtracting fractions to include adding and subtracting mixed numbers. You will also work with your team to use your new skills to decipher clues and navigate a treasure map, avoiding terrible danger to find the Treasure of Tragon.

Guiding Questions

Think about these questions throughout this chapter:

What can I measure?

Is there another way to see it?

How can I represent it?

How can I rewrite them using like parts?

How can I estimate it?

In this chapter, you will learn how to:

➢ Find the volume of some three-dimensional shapes, known as right prisms.

➢ Find common denominators.

➢ Add and subtract fractions, decimals, and mixed numbers.

➢ **Make sense** of the traditional algorithm for long division.

➢ Represent addition and subtraction of fractions using diagrams.

➢ Use mental math strategies to add and subtract fractions, decimals, and mixed numbers.

➢ Estimate sums and differences of fractions.

Chapter Outline

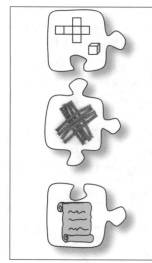

Section 7.1   You will learn about volume and surface area of three-dimensional shapes. You will develop strategies for calculating volume and surface area of prisms.

Section 7.2   You will divide different amounts of licorice among different numbers of people. You will develop strategies to add fractions and subtract fractions. You will estimate sums and differences of fractions and use mental math strategies to add and subtract them without having to write anything down.

Section 7.3   You will extend your understanding to include adding and subtracting mixed numbers and practice your new skills as you decipher clues to help you navigate treacherous terrain to find the Treasure of Tragon.

    Making Connections: Course 1

7.1.1 What can I measure?

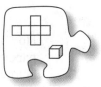

Introduction to Volume and Surface Area

If an object, such as a line, has length but no width and no height, it is said to be of **one dimension**. If an object has length and width but no height, such as a figure drawn on paper, it is said to be of **two dimensions**. If an object has length, width and height, such as a box, it is said to be of **three dimensions**. In this section, you will consider measurements related to **three-dimensional** objects.

7-1.   WHICH IS BIGGER?

Your teacher will show you two boxes. Which box is bigger? What is bigger about it? Be ready to share your ideas with the class.

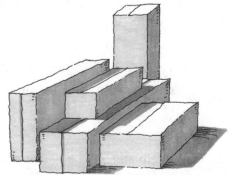

7-2.   What can we measure about a box? With your team, brainstorm as many things as possible that you can measure about a box. For each of your ideas, name a tool you could use to make such a measurement. Be ready to add your ideas to a class list.

7-3.   In Chapter 2, you learned about measuring length with a ruler. For length, you used units such as inches, centimeters, and miles. In Chapter 3, you learned about measuring area using square units on a grid or by calculating based on multiplication. For area, you used square units such as square inches, square centimeters, and square miles. For a three-dimensional object, the **surface area** is defined as the combined areas of each of its surfaces (called **faces**). The amount of space that a three-dimensional object takes up is called its **volume**. To measure volume, you need units that measure the three-dimensions of space (length, width, and height), so you will use **cubic units**.

Obtain Lesson 7.1.1 Resource Pages from your teacher. Work with your team to cut out the four small nets, then fold and tape them to create cubic units. Then cut out each of the larger nets, fold and tape them to create boxes, known as **right rectangular prisms**.

Problem continues on next page →

7-3.   *Problem continued from previous page.*

How many cubic units does it take to fill each box? What is the total area of the paper it takes to make each box? Record your results in a table such as the one below.

Length	Width	Height	Volume (in cubic units)	Surface Area (in square units)

7-4.   Jeremiah was working on building the boxes in problem 7-3, when he noticed that he could calculate surface area of each box from its net *before* he built the box. How could he do this?

7-5.   Jeremiah built a box that was 5 units long by 6 units wide by 7 units high. He placed the box on a surface that measured 5 units by 6 units and started filling it with cubes. He realized quickly that he did not have nearly enough cubes to fill the box. Can he still figure out how many cubes it would hold? Discuss this with your team and be ready to **explain** your ideas to the class.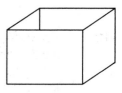

7-6.   Imagine a cube that is 1 cm wide, 1 cm high, and 1 cm long.

a.   Sketch the cube on your paper.

b.   What is the volume of this cube?

c.   What is the surface area of this cube?

7-7.   Draw a square like the one at the right, and shade a portion that represents 76%. Write the portion as a fraction and a decimal.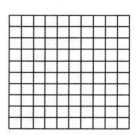

7-8.   The table at right shows all possible kinds of sandwiches at Dane's Deli.

	Ham	Turkey	Roast Beef
Wheat Bread			
White Bread			

   a.   How many different combinations of sandwiches are possible? List the options.

   b.   If you reach into a picnic basket that contains one of each kind of sandwich, what is your chance of getting a turkey sandwich on wheat bread?

7-9.   Wendy and Peter each made up a new *"Guess My Decimal"* game just for you. Use their clues to determine the number.

   a.   Wendy gives you the clue, *"The decimal I am thinking about is seven-tenths greater than 46%. What is my decimal?"* Show your work.

   b.   Peter continues the game with the following clue, *"My decimal is six-hundredths less than five-tenths."* Use pictures and/or words to show your thinking.

7-10.   For each of the following problems, complete the fraction on the right so that the fractions are equal. Be sure to show your work clearly.

   a. $\frac{3}{5} = \frac{}{30}$ b. $\frac{65}{100} = \frac{}{20}$ c. $\frac{1}{2} = \frac{}{888}$

7-11.   Draw any quadrilateral (a four-sided polygon). Enlarge it by a ratio of $\frac{7}{2}$. Record the lengths of the sides of the original and the new quadrilateral on your drawing.

7.1.2 How can I find the volume?

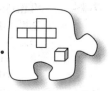

Volume of Right Prisms

In the previous lesson, you calculated volumes and surface areas of prisms. In this lesson, you will continue to examine these concepts as you work with your team to find ways to calculate volume without having to do a lot of counting.

7-12. Carly and Stella are studying to be architects. They have been asked to design an office building. They have come up with five possible floor plans below.

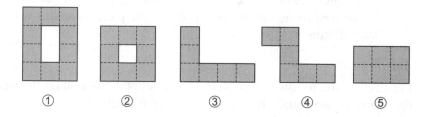

① ② ③ ④ ⑤

They have not yet decided how many stories high they want to make each building, but they would like all of the buildings to hold a similar number of offices.

a. Use cubes to build a model of the first floor of each building. If each office takes up one cubic unit, how many offices will fit on this floor?

b. Your teacher will assign your team one building to examine further. For this building, build the second floor. How many offices would fit in this building if it were two stories high?

c. Add a third floor. How many offices would fit in this one?

d. What would be the volume of this building if it were 9 floors high? How can you figure this out without building it?

7-13. Organize your data into a table showing the relationship between the number of floors (also called "stories") and the number of offices (or volume) in your building. How can you **describe** the relationship?

7-14.   Carly and Stella have learned that their building can have no more than
         195 offices. How many stories high could they make their building if they used
         the floor plan your teacher assigned you?

7-15.   Carly and Stella want to make the **lateral surfaces** (the sides that are not the
         floor or the ceiling) of the whole building entirely out of glass. How much glass
         will they need for their building if they use the floor plan your teacher assigned
         you and the heights you found in problem 7-14? Be prepared to **explain** your
         result to the class.

7-16.   George was working with Building 1 from problem 7-12. The
         floor plan is reprinted at right. He built the first floor using cubes
         and found that the volume was 10 cubic units.

         "Wait," he said. *"I can see by looking at the floor plan, that the
         area is 10 square units. Why are the area and volume both equal to 10?"*

         Is this a coincidence? Investigate this with your team. Will the area of the floor
         plan always have the same numerical value as the volume of the first floor?
         Explain why your answer **makes sense**.

7-17.   The shaded figure at right is two-dimensional and has an area of
         12 square units. If it is the base of a prism with a height of 7 units,
         what is the volume of the prism? **Explain** how you know.

7-18.   If a 3-story building has a volume of 24 cubic units, what would the volume be
         if it were 5 stories high?

7-19.   LEARNING LOG

         How can you calculate the volume of *any* building if you
         know the height and the area of its base? Discuss this
         question with your team and be ready to **explain** your ideas
         to the class. Then record your ideas in a Learning Log entry.
         Title this entry "Volume of Prisms" and label it with today's date.

7-20.   Find the volume of the right prism shown at right if the area
         of the base is 8 square units.

7-21. Use a Giant One to change each of the following fractions to a number written as a fraction over 100. Then write each portion as a percent.

a. $\frac{3}{20}$

b. $\frac{3}{40}$

7-22. Find the area of the shape at right. All angles are right angles.

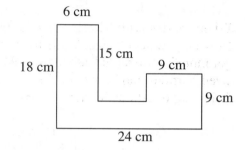

7-23. Simplify the following expressions and then check your answers with a scientific calculator.

a. $(16+2) \cdot (-3-1)$

b. $-6+7 \cdot 5$

c. $4(-6)-(-11)+6(1-5)$

7-24. Complete each of the webs below.

a.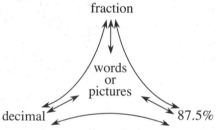

Representations of a Portion

b.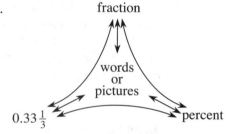

Representations of a Portion

7-25. Some of the axes and graphs below have errors and some do not. Decide if everything is done correctly or not. If there are errors, redraw the entire graph correctly.

a.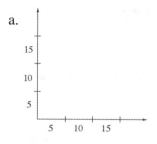

b.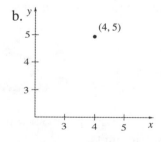

c.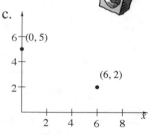

7.2.1 How can I share it equally?

Dividing and Partitioning

When sharing with friends, how do you know if everyone is getting the same amount? How do you decide to split the item(s) being shared? Have you ever argued about who got more? In today's lesson, you will explore how to divide pieces of licorice into equally sized portions and how to deal fairly with any "leftovers." As you work, keep the following questions in mind:

How can we represent (show) it?

How can we tell which portions are the same amount?

Is there another way to share?

7-26.   FAIR SHARES

How would your team share 5 pieces of licorice? What about 7 pieces? Today you will work with a new team to **describe** how to distribute the licorice fairly among different numbers of people.

Your task: For each situation below, **explain** at least one way to share the licorice fairly among all team members. For each case, represent the amount of licorice each team member will receive with pictures, words, and numbers.

Team W has 3 members and gets 5 pieces of licorice.

Team X has 5 members and gets 9 pieces of licorice.

Team Y has 6 members and gets 10 pieces of licorice.

7-27.   With your team, prepare a poster and a presentation that **explains** how to divide *your team's* licorice among your team members. In other words, if you are in a W team, you will **explain** how to divide 5 pieces of licorice among 3 team members. Be sure to plan your presentation so that each member of your team has a chance to **explain** something mathematically meaningful. Your poster (and presentation) should include:

- Pictures, numbers, words (and perhaps straws) that **explain** what portion of a whole piece of licorice each person gets.

- An **explanation** of how you know that you are sharing fairly.

7-28.   Consider all of the strategies to share licorice that are presented by your classmates.

a.   If your teacher passed out licorice this way, would it be fair? In other words, do all students in the class get the same amount of licorice using the strategies developed by your classmates? How can you tell?

b.   How else could the licorice be distributed? Is there a way so that everyone gets an equal part? Find as many ways as you can to show what you mean.

7-29.   If you were given a choice to receive one of the following lengths of licorice, which would you choose? Be prepared to **explain** your decision.

Option #1: $\frac{3}{5}$ of a piece and $\frac{2}{7}$ of a piece.

Option #2: $\frac{7}{10}$ of a piece and $\frac{1}{3}$ of a piece.

METHODS AND MEANINGS

Volume of Right Prisms

The length of a segment is the number of segments of length 1 that are needed to cover it exactly. The area of a region is the number of squares of area 1 that are needed to cover it exactly. Similarly the **volume** of a solid is the number of cubes of volume 1 that are needed to fill it exactly.

The volume of a right rectangular prism (which looks like a standard box) can be computed with the formula:

Volume = (Area of base)·height.

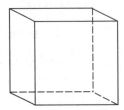

In this case, the **base** is covered with the squares that are the bases of the cubes in the first layer. The number of these cubes is the same as the area of the base. The **height** is the number of cubes that are needed to form a stack of cubes from the bottom to the top of the box. The number of cubes needed to fill the prism is the number of layers of cubes (height) times the number of cubes in each layer (area of the base).

The same formula works for other figures that are right prisms:

Volume = (Area of base)·height.

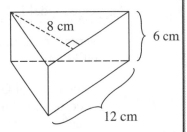

The right prism shown in the diagram at right has a height of 6 cm and a triangular base with an area of 48 sq cm. To calculate its volume, multiply the area of the base times the height of the prism, or
48 sq cm · 6 cm = 288 cu cm.

7-30.   If you had 2 pieces of licorice to share equally among three people, how much licorice would each person get? Show your thinking clearly.

7-31.   Jill sees a bed and a desk that she would like to buy for her bedroom, but she is worried that they may not fit along the same wall. The tags say that the bed is 40 inches wide and the desk is 152 centimeters wide.

   a.   What does Jill need to do before she can figure out the total width of the bed and the desk together?

   b.   Jill sees a chart that tells her than 1 centimeter is approximately equal to 0.3937 inches and 1 inch is approximately equal to 2.54 centimeters. Help Jill figure out the combined width of the bed and the desk expressed in both inches and centimeters.

   c.   If Jill knows that the wall in her room is 9.5 feet long, can she fit both the bed and the desk along the wall? How can you be sure?

7-32.   Calculate each of the following parts of parts.

   a. $\frac{2}{3}$ of $\frac{3}{7}$ b. $\frac{1}{6}$ of $\frac{11}{12}$

7-33.   Glenda made a scale model of the Empire State Building in New York. The building itself is 1250 feet high and her scale model is 5 feet high.

   a.   Write a ratio to **compare** the heights of the two buildings.

   b.   If the entry of Glenda's model is 2 inches wide, how wide would you expect the entry of the real building to be?

   c.   If the real building contains 102 floors, how many floors should Glenda's model contain?

7-34.   Draw or **describe** the dimensions of *at least two* prisms with volume of 100 cubic units.

Making Connections: Course 1

7-35.   If you had 12 pieces of licorice to share equally among 5 people, how much licorice would each person get? Be sure to show your thinking clearly.

7-36.   Greg is building a fence. He places two sections end to end. One section measures 3 meters and the other measures 120 centimeters.

   a.   Greg thinks the fence will be 123 units long, but is not sure what the units are. His sister Elisa thinks he is wrong. What do you think? **Explain**.

   b.   Find at least two ways to express the length of the fence.

7-37.   For each of the following multiplication problems, first estimate the product. Then check your estimation by multiplying.

   a. $\frac{1}{2} \cdot \frac{6}{5}$ b. $\frac{4}{5} \cdot \frac{8}{9}$ c. $\frac{3}{7} \cdot \frac{1}{2}$

7-38.   For each of the following questions, draw a diagram to **explain** your answer.

   a.   How many fourths are in one-half?

   b.   How many sixths are in two-thirds?

   c.   How many fourths are in six-eighths?

   d.   How many halves are in $3\frac{5}{10}$?

7-39.   Estimate the measure of the angle shown at right.

7-40.   Use the numbers 0, 1, 2, $2\frac{1}{2}$, 3, 7, $7\frac{1}{2}$, 9, and 10 to answer each of the following questions. Note that you may use each number as many times as you like.

   a.   List five numbers with a mean of 5.

   b.   List five numbers with a mean of 5 and a median of $2\frac{1}{2}$.

   c.   If a list of five numbers has a mean of 5, what is the largest median that this set of data can have?

7.2.2 How can I name this portion?

Adding Fractions

In Lesson 7.2.1, you found **multiple ways** to represent the result of dividing different amounts of licorice evenly among different numbers of students. In this lesson, you will find strategies to name some of the amounts as single fractions.

7-41.   James and Janea were trying to figure out how to divide 7 pieces of licorice among 5 students. Janea made the first suggestion.

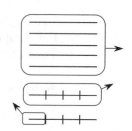

"Look," she said. *"If each person gets a whole piece, then there are 2 pieces left. Let's start by giving each person another quarter of a piece."* She drew the diagram at right to show her thinking.

"Okay," James said. *"Now we have $\frac{3}{4}$ of a piece left for 5 people, so shouldn't each person get $\frac{1}{5}$ of that $\frac{3}{4}$?"*

    a.   Do you agree with James? If so, help him to figure out what size piece is $\frac{1}{5}$ of $\frac{3}{4}$. If not, **explain** what he should do.

    b.   How much licorice would each student have? Express your answer as a sum of the parts of licorice each person will have.

    c.   Work with your team to estimate about how much licorice each student is getting using this method. Is it close to 2 pieces? Is it close to $1\frac{1}{2}$ pieces? How can you tell?

7-42.   In problem 7-41, you thought about one way to divide 7 lengths of licorice among 5 people equally. What would happen if each of the licorice pieces were split into 5 equal parts and these parts were given out?

    a.   How many pieces would each person get? What would be the length of each part?

    b.   One way to write the amount each person gets in part (a) is $7(\frac{1}{5})$ or $\frac{7}{5}$. This is different from James and Janea's expression (from problem 7-41). Did James and Janea make a mistake? Why does their answer look so different?

Problem continues on next page →

Making Connections: Course 1

7-42. *Problem continued from previous page.*

    c.   Use the Dynamic Tool (as shown by your teacher) to enter James and Janea's answer. Then work with t he tool to cut each of the licorice segments from their answer into pieces that are the same size so that the whole length can be expressed as one fraction. What is another way to write the sum?

7-43.   James and Janea were working on problem 7-42, when Janea noticed something. *"Look,"* she said. *"When each of the fractions is broken into the same sized pieces, the denominators are all the same."*

    "Yes," James said. *"But how do we know what the denominators will be?"*

    For parts (a), (b), and (c):

- *Estimate* each sum, using words such as *"slightly more than 1"*, *"slightly less than $\frac{1}{2}$ "*, etc.
- Use the Dynamic Tool to check your ideas and then find the sums.
- What denominators did you use to add each of pair of fractions? Was there more than one possibility? Be prepared to **explain** your reasoning.

    a. $\frac{4}{5}+1\frac{1}{10}$ b. $\frac{5}{12}+\frac{2}{3}$ c. $\frac{2}{3}+\frac{3}{4}$

7-44.   David wants to find $\frac{3}{10}+\frac{21}{100}$ and is wondering if using decimals can help him **make sense** of adding fractions.

    a.   How could $\frac{3}{10}+\frac{21}{100}$ be written using decimals? What is the sum as a decimal?

    b.   How could your answer from part (a) be written as a fraction?

    c.   Rewrite $\frac{3}{10}$ as a fraction that could be added easily to $\frac{21}{100}$.

7-45.   Angelica does not like licorice and has decided to give her $1\frac{2}{3}$ pieces to Terrinika, who already has $1\frac{4}{5}$ pieces. Work with your team to figure out how much licorice Terrinika will have. Be prepared to share your results.

7-46.   Which of the following fractions could you add together easily? **Explain.**

$$\frac{5}{7}, \frac{2}{3}, \frac{1}{4}, \frac{4}{3}, \frac{7}{5}, \frac{1}{2}, \frac{9}{10}, \frac{1}{5}, \frac{5}{6}, \frac{1}{7}, \frac{2}{2}$$

7-47.   For each description of fractions below, write a statement about the relative sizes of the denominators. An example statement might be, *"The denominator of Fraction X is three times the size of the denominator of Fraction Y."*

  - Are the numbers in the denominators the same?
  - If not, which number is larger in value?
  - How much larger?

  a.   Fraction A and Fraction B are made up of pieces that are the same size.

  b.   Fraction C is made up of pieces that are half the size of Fraction D.

  c.   Five of the pieces of Fraction E would fit into each of the pieces of Fraction F.

7-48.   What is the sum of $\frac{2}{2} + \frac{3}{3}$? Represent your ideas in **multiple ways**.

7-49.   The first four multiples of 5 are: 5, 10, 15, and 20.

  a.   What are the first six multiples of 10?

  b.   What are the first six multiples of 8?

  c.   What is the Least Common Multiple (the lowest number that is a multiple of both numbers) of 10 and 8?

7-50.   If you had 5 pieces of licorice to share equally among 7 people, how much licorice would each person get? Show a diagram of how you would cut the licorice for each person.

7-51.   Use a Giant One to change each of the following fractions to a number over 100. Then write each portion as a percent.

  a. $\frac{85}{200}$ b. $\frac{17}{15}$

Making Connections: Course 1

7-52.   Copy and complete each of the Diamond Problems below.
         The pattern used in the Diamond Problems is shown at right.

a.   b.   c.   d.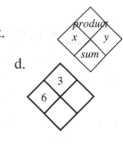

7-53.   Which is larger, $\frac{3}{4}$ or $\frac{11}{16}$? How can you be sure?

7-54.   Mr. Nowlin has a rectangular garden with an area of 45 square feet and a length
         of 10 feet.

         a. What is the width of the garden?   b. What is the garden's perimeter?

7-55.   Figure out whether each of the following pairs of fractions are equivalent. Be
         sure to show all of your work or **explain** your thinking clearly.

         a. $\frac{3}{4}$ and $\frac{75}{100}$ b. $\frac{2}{3}$ and $\frac{12}{13}$ c. $\frac{8}{5}$ and $\frac{5}{8}$

7-56.   Place the following fractions in order from least to greatest: $\frac{2}{5}, 1\frac{1}{3}, \frac{7}{4}, \frac{1}{16}, \frac{7}{8}$.

7-57.   Find the area and perimeter of the figure shown at
         right. All angles are right angles. Show your work
         clearly.

7-58.   The table below shows the results from repeated
         spins of a mystery spinner. Sketch a possible
         spinner with the experimental probability written in
         each part.

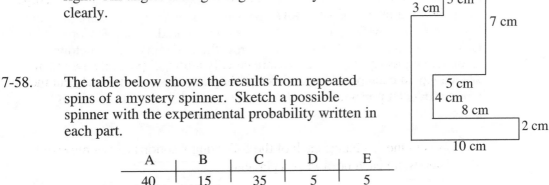

A	B	C	D	E
40	15	35	5	5

7-59.   What are the next three numbers in the pattern: 1, 3, 7, 13, 21, …?
         Describe the pattern in words.

Connecting Fractions and Division

In Lesson 7.2.1, you worked with your team to divide pieces of licorice evenly among several people. You have probably worked with division problems in the past that asked you to find, for example, how many teams of 3 students could be formed from a class of 36 students, or if 24 eggs were divided evenly into 2 cartons, how many eggs should be in each carton. You may also have learned how to do more complicated division calculations such as $208 \div 16$ using methods such as long division.

How are division problems like these and the problem of dividing licorice related? Can your methods and thinking in one situation be used to find solutions in the other? Think about the following focus questions as you work with your team on the problems in this lesson.

What does this represent?

How does this connect to what we already know how to do?

How can we apply this strategy?

7-60.   When using the Dynamic Tool to do problem 7-42, one of the students in Ms. Nikula's class exclaimed, *"Whoa! We divided 7 pieces of licorice among 5 people and the answer is $\frac{7}{5}$. Is this just a coincidence?"*

What do you think? Does it **make sense** that the numbers here are the same? What if, for example, 4 pieces of licorice were shared among 3 people? Different teams in Ms. Nikula's class drew the diagrams shown below.

Work with your team to **make sense** of their diagrams. Did each team get the same answer? How were they thinking about dividing the licorice? Be prepared to share your ideas with the whole class.

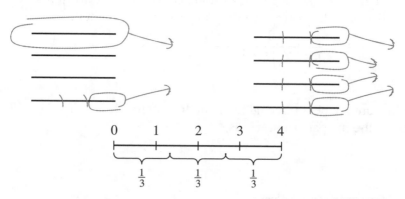

7-61.   Will these diagramming strategies work for any numbers? Work with your team to use each of the strategies shown in problem 7-60 to do the following problems, if you can. If a particular strategy does not **make sense** for one of the problems, **explain** why it does not.

   a.   Show how to divide 9 pieces of licorice among 4 people.

   b.   Show how to divide 3 pieces of licorice among 4 people.

   c.   Is there a connection between the operation of division and a fraction? Discuss this with your team and be prepared to **explain** your ideas to the class.

7-62.   Two methods to calculate 7 divided by 5 are shown below. The work on the left uses long division and the work on the right uses a diagram. Work with your team to **make sense** of the two methods by answering the questions that follow.

   a.   What does the 1 written at the top of the division calculation at right represent in terms of sharing licorice? How can you see the same 1 in the diagram?

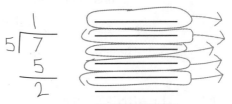

   b.   What does the 2 written at the bottom of the division calculation represent? How can you see the 2 in the diagram?

   c.   The next step of the division calculation is shown at right. What is done in this step? How can you see the same step in the diagram? That is, where is the 20 and how is it created? What does the 20 mean?

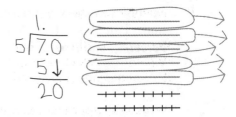

   d.   Copy the long division problem and the diagram onto your paper and finish them. For each step, **explain** the connections between the two methods. How much licorice would each person get all together?

7-63.   Since the problems about dividing licorice resulted in answers that could be written as single fractions, Lalo began to wonder about the connection between division and fractions. Lalo said to his team, *"Since division problems result in a fraction, maybe fractions represent division."*

a.   With your team, discuss how you could use Lalo's idea to write $\frac{7}{20}$ as a division problem.

b.   Use your calculator to find the decimal that results from the division problem you wrote in part (a)?

c.   Follow these directions to write each of the following fractions as decimals.

- First estimate the size of each number by marking its place on a number line.

- Write the division problem that the fraction could represent.

- Then use your calculator to do the division and find the decimal representation. How close were your estimates?

i. $\frac{23}{8}$ *ii.* $\frac{18}{25}$

7-64.   LEARNING LOG

What methods do you know to convert fractions to decimals or percents? Discuss this with your team and then make up examples to show in your Learning Log each method you find. Title this entry "Converting Fractions to Decimals and Percents" and label it with today's date.

MᴇᴛHODS AND Mᴇᴀɴɪɴɢs

MATH NOTES

Dividing Decimals by Integers

You may know how to divide one number by another using long division. When using long division, it is important to be sure that you know the place value of each digit in your result.

In our example of dividing 225 by 6, people often say *"6 goes into 22 three times,"* although *"6 goes into 220 thirty-some times"* is a better description of what is taking place in this calculation. The 3 of the quotient is written in the tens place to indicate that 6 goes into 225 at least 30 times, but less than 40.

The 3 then multiplies the divisor and the product is placed below the 22. Then subtract, getting 4, "bring down" the 5, to get 45, and repeat the same process. In the past, you may have stopped the process at this point, and written that the quotient is 37 with a remainder of 3.

The same method works for dividing a decimal. Our second example is essentially the same as the first, except that we keep dividing even when we get to the decimal point.

$$
\begin{array}{r}
37 \\
6\overline{)225} \\
18\downarrow \\
\overline{45} \\
42 \\
\overline{3}
\end{array}
\qquad
\begin{array}{r}
3.75 \\
6\overline{)22.50} \\
18 \\
\overline{45} \\
42 \\
\overline{30} \\
30 \\
\overline{0}
\end{array}
$$

7-65.   Use your understanding of equivalent fractions to write two fractions that are equivalent to each of the following fractions.

a. $\frac{1}{2}$ b. $\frac{3}{5}$ c. $\frac{4}{7}$

7-66.   Cisco and Janet spent an afternoon making burritos and put them all on one plate. Six burritos have beef inside, 17 have chicken filling, and 2 have black bean filling. Find the probability of randomly choosing the following burritos, and write your answer as a fraction, decimal, and percent.

a.   A burrito with black bean filling.

b.   A burrito that does *not* have beef filling.

7-67.   Find the **least common multiple** of the following pairs of numbers. In other words, find the smallest number that is a multiple of both of the numbers in the pair.

a.   3 and 24   b.   7 and 9   c.   15 and 12

7-68.   Without a calculator, add each of the following sets of decimals.

a. $1.2 + 3.04$ b. $0.85 + 4.1$

7-69.   Draw a generic rectangle to show the product of $3\frac{1}{7} \cdot 4\frac{2}{3}$. Calculate each of the areas of the rectangle and then estimate their sum.

7-70.   Find each of the products in parts (a) through (d) below.

a. $\frac{2}{3} \cdot \frac{2}{7}$ b. $\frac{4}{7} \cdot \frac{3}{4}$ c. $\frac{10}{13} \cdot \frac{3}{5}$ d. $1\frac{2}{3} \cdot \frac{1}{5}$

7.2.4 How can I tell what size will work?

Common Denominators

In Lesson 7.2.2, you recognized that in order to add fractions, each one must be cut into pieces that are the same size. You used a Dynamic Tool to help you figure out what size pieces would work. In this lesson, you will cut fractions into pieces of the same size without using a Dynamic Tool. As you work with your team, keep the following questions in mind.

What part of the fraction tells me what size the pieces are?

How do the numbers in the fraction change if I cut each piece in half?
In thirds? In fourths, etc.?

Is it equivalent?

7-71. Helen and Grace were cleaning up from their class pizza party. They combined into one box a half of a pizza and a quarter of another pizza. Helen said, *"Isn't this $\frac{1}{2}+\frac{1}{4}$?"* Grace said. *"We don't need the Dynamic Tool to add these fractions! We can see that $\frac{1}{2}+\frac{1}{4}=\frac{3}{4}$."*

a. Why is there a 3 in the answer to $\frac{1}{2}+\frac{1}{4}$?

b. What other fractional parts could help you add these fractions? For example, could each fraction be represented with eighths ($\frac{1}{8}$)? Thousandths ($\frac{1}{1000}$)? Work with your team to decide whether these could work. Would you get the same answer? Try it.

7-72. Now work with your team to rewrite fractions so that they are represented with the same-sized parts, as you did with the Dynamic Tool in Lesson 7.2.2. Another way to say this is that you will express two or more fractions with a **common denominator**. For each of the fraction sums below:

- Without writing, make an estimate of the sum. Will it be more than one? Less than one? Around a half? Close to zero? For each sum, be ready to **explain** your thinking.

- Then rewrite each sum as the sum of fractions with the same denominator. Again, be prepared to **explain** your strategies to the class.

- Add the fractions and simplify your result.

    a. $\frac{2}{3}+\frac{1}{9}$ b. $\frac{3}{4}+\frac{5}{6}$ c. $\frac{1}{3}+\frac{4}{7}$

7-73.   Murph and Hanson were working on problem 7-72, when Murph had an idea.
         "I wonder," he said, *"if we can use an area model to figure out the sizes of
         pieces that we need for these fractions. How could we try it for $\frac{3}{4}+\frac{5}{6}$?"*

         "Let's start by drawing $\frac{3}{4}$," said Hanson as he drew the
         diagram at right. *"Now how can we figure out what size
         pieces will work also with sixths?"*

         "I have an idea." said Murph. *"What if we split the
         rectangle into sixths in the other direction like this?
         Then we can see that $\frac{3}{4}$ is equal to $\frac{18}{24}$."*

         "Okay," said Hanson. *"Let's see if this works
         for $\frac{5}{6}$ also. We can start by drawing $\frac{5}{6}$ like
         this and then break them into fourths. Then we
         can see that $\frac{5}{6}$ is equal to $\frac{20}{24}$."*

         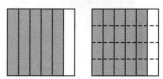

         a.   Work with your team to finish Murph and Hanson's work to add $\frac{3}{4}+\frac{5}{6}$.
              Does the result agree with the one you got in part (b) of problem 7-72?
              Explain.

         b.   Draw an area model to help you add $\frac{1}{3}+\frac{4}{7}$. Check that your answer agrees
              with the one you got for part (c) of problem 7-72.

7-74.   As you have discovered, any fraction can be rewritten in many equivalent ways.
         When choosing a denominator that will work to add two fractions, there is no
         single correct choice. Often people find it convenient to use the smallest whole
         number that all denominators divide into evenly. This number is called the
         lowest common denominator.

         For example, when adding the fractions $\frac{2}{3}+\frac{5}{6}+\frac{3}{8}$, you could choose to rewrite
         each fraction as some number of 48[th]s or 96[th]s, but the numbers will stay smaller
         if you choose to rewrite each fraction as some number of 24[th]s, since 24 is the
         lowest number that 3, 6, and 8 divide into evenly (that is, without a remainder).

         For each of the following sums, rewrite each fraction using the **lowest common
         denominator** and then add.

         a. $\frac{5}{12}+\frac{1}{3}$ b. $\frac{4}{5}+\frac{3}{4}$

7-75.   You may remember that you have seen sums of fractions before that you were, at that time, only able to estimate using generic rectangles to multiply mixed numbers. Can your new knowledge of adding fractions help you to use generic rectangles to multiply mixed numbers? Think about the product $4\frac{2}{5} \cdot 3\frac{1}{3}$.

   a.   Draw a generic rectangle to find this product. Write your answer as the sum of all of the parts of the rectangle.

   b.   With your team, discuss how you can add the four areas to get an answer that is one number. Then find the sum.

   c.   Another way to find the product $4\frac{2}{5} \cdot 3\frac{1}{3}$ is to rewrite both mixed numbers as fractions greater than one and then to multiply these. Use this method to find the answer.

   d.   Which method do you prefer? Why?

7-76.   Work with your team to find each of the following sums.

   a. $\frac{2}{3} + \frac{1}{2}$,

   b. $\frac{1}{4} + \frac{1}{6} + \frac{3}{8}$

7-77.   James noticed that his ruler includes eighths and sixteenths of an inch. Help him to make the following conversions.

   a. $\frac{2}{16} = \frac{\square}{8}$

   b. $\frac{4}{16} = \frac{\square}{8}$

   c. $\frac{10}{16} = \frac{\square}{8}$

   d. $\frac{18}{16} = \frac{\square}{8}$

   e.   In general, if you have any number if sixteenths, how can you figure out how many eighths you have?

7-78.   Find common denominators in order to calculate each of the following sums.

   a. $\frac{3}{8} + \frac{1}{4}$

   b. $\frac{2}{5} + \frac{1}{3}$

7-79.   Consider the diagram of three pieces of lumber shown at right.

$$\underline{\quad 4 \quad} \quad \underline{\quad\quad x \quad\quad} \quad \underline{\quad\quad x \quad\quad}$$

   a.   If $x = 6$ meters, how long are all three pieces of lumber laid end to end?

   b.   If the total length of all three pieces laid end to end is 20 meters, what is the value of x?

7-80. Find the volume of the prism shown at right if the area of the base is 14 square feet.

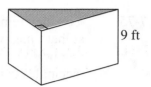

9 ft

7-81. Simplify each of the following expressions.

a. $\frac{7 \cdot 3 + 5}{2}$

b. $3 + 8 \div 4 - 1$

c. $2(12 - 4) + 4$

d. $4(9 + 3) + 10 \div 2$

7-82. **Multiple Choice:** The sum of $\frac{15}{16} + \frac{6}{5} + \frac{6}{7} + \frac{5}{6}$ is *approximately* equal to which of the following whole numbers? Write a sentence **explaining** your answer.

A. 1   B. 2   C. 3   D. 4

7.2.5 What is the difference?

Subtracting Fractions and Decimals

In Lesson 7.2.1, when you figured out how to divide licorice among differently sized teams, was the result fair? That is, did students in every team receive the same amount? Did they receive close to the same amount? In this lesson, you will use the ideas you have learned to develop strategies for finding the difference between (or subtracting) two fractions.

7-83. WHO GOT MORE? HOW MUCH MORE?

In Lesson 7.2.1, you found that the "fair shares" described in problem 7-26 were not truly fair. For example, each of the students in Team W received $\frac{5}{3}$ of a piece of licorice, while each of the students in Team X received $\frac{9}{5}$ of a piece.

a. Which students received more licorice? How can you tell?

b. Work with your team to find the exact difference between $\frac{5}{3}$ and $\frac{9}{5}$. Be prepared to share your ideas with the class.

c. When you want the difference between $\frac{5}{3}$ and $\frac{9}{5}$, should you write $\frac{5}{3} - \frac{9}{5}$ or $\frac{9}{5} - \frac{5}{3}$? Why?

Discussion Points

How can we draw this problem?

How can we **compare** them if they are in pieces of different sizes?

7-84.   One way to calculate $\frac{9}{5}-\frac{5}{3}$ is to use area models to represent the fractions. One possible picture is shown below right.

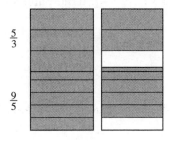

   a.   Look at these diagrams with your team. Do they support your answer for part (a) of problem 7-83? **Explain.**

   b.   Each of these fractions is a whole plus some part less than one. Since you are finding the difference, do you need to be concerned about the two wholes? That is, can you just find the difference between the two parts that are less than one? Why or why not?

   c.   If you remove the parts of the diagrams that represent one for each fraction, what will be left? How can you break these into the same size pieces, similar to when you were adding fractions?

   d.   Work with your team to rename each of the fractions with their new part size and find the difference.

———————   *Further Guidance*   ———————
            section ends here.

7-85.   As you recall, in problem 7-28, the whole class put all of the licorice together and divided it equally among all students. Which team(s) (W, X, or Y) benefited from this? In other words, which students got more when the whole class shared all of it? Which students got less? How much more or less?

   a.   Look back at your work from Lesson 7.2.1. When the available licorice was shared with the class, how much licorice did each person receive?

   b.   **Compare** this amount with the amounts received by Teams W, X, and Y in problem 7-26. For each team, state which sharing strategy gives them more licorice and use your new subtraction strategy to find a fraction that **describes** each difference.

   c.   Which team benefited the most from the whole class sharing fairly? How can you tell?

7-86.   You have figured out how to add and subtract many different fractions. How can you **describe** the process of adding or subtracting *any* fractions?

   a.   Work with your team to write instructions for a new student about how to add and subtract fractions.

   b.   Test your instructions by trying to follow them while doing these problems. If you find any steps missing in your instructions, go back and add them to the instructions. Be prepared to share your ideas with the class.

   i. $\frac{2}{3} - \frac{1}{6}$ *ii.* $\frac{5}{6} + \frac{3}{8}$ *iii.* $\frac{3}{5} - \frac{2}{7}$

7-87.   LEARNING LOG

Contribute your ideas to a class discussion to generate a complete and correct set of instructions for adding and subtracting fractions. Then copy these instructions into your Learning Log. Title this entry, "Adding and Subtracting Fractions" and label it with today's date.

7-88.   Does $10 + \frac{2}{7} = \frac{12}{7}$? **Explain** why or why not.

7-89.   Add each of the following expressions to show each student's portion of licorice with a single fraction.

   a.   Students in Team W got $1 + \frac{1}{2} + \frac{1}{6}$.

   b.   Students in Team X got $1 + \frac{1}{2} + \frac{1}{5} + \frac{1}{10}$.

   c.   Students in Team Y got $1 + \frac{1}{6} + \frac{1}{6} + \frac{1}{6} + \frac{1}{6}$.

7-90.   Complete each of the calculations.

   a. $\frac{2}{3} - \frac{5}{12}$ b. $\frac{4}{5} + \frac{11}{12}$

7-91.   Where should each of the fractions described below be on a number line? For each one, include an example to support your ideas.

   a.   The numerator is very small compared to the size of the denominator.

   b.   The numerator is about half the size of the denominator.

   c.   The numerator is about the same size as the denominator.

   d.   The numerator is much larger than the denominator.

7-92.   A triangle has a base of 16 cm and a height of 8 cm. A triangle with the same shape has a base of 6.4 cm and a height of 3.2 cm. What is the ratio of sides?

7-93.   Hector is using radar to monitor speeds on a street near his school. He records the following speeds, each in miles per hour: 34, 35, 39, 40, 36, 35, 55, 42, 35, and 39.

   a.   What is the mean of these speeds?

   b.   What is the median?

   c.   What is the mode?

   d.   Hector wants to show the city council that there is a speeding problem. Which of the measures of central tendency that you calculated above should he use? **Explain** why.

7-94.   Use mental math strategies to solve the following problems in your head. Record the strategy that you used for each problem and the answer.

   a. $275 + 187$ b. $201 - 97$ c. $26 + 129$

7.3.1   What if they are bigger than one?

Adding and Subtracting Mixed Numbers

Throughout this chapter, you have learned methods to add and subtract fractions and decimals. But what if you are working with numbers that are larger than one? In this lesson, you will work with your team to consider this question. As you work on the problems in this lesson, keep the following questions in mind:

How big should the answer be?

Does our answer **make sense**?

Is there another way to do it?

7-95.   WHY DO WE REGROUP?

Kelly and Mishka were working on finding the difference between $\frac{7}{10}$ and $\frac{13}{100}$. Kelly thought that since these fractions are tenths and hundredths, it could be convenient to represent this difference using hundredths grids.

a.   Get a strip of hundredths grids from your teacher. On the first two grids, draw $\frac{7}{10}$ and $\frac{13}{100}$. Then, on the third grid, find a way to represent the difference. How can you name this difference? In other words, what is $\frac{7}{10} - \frac{13}{100}$?

b.   Mishka decided to represent these numbers as decimals and subtract them that way. He wrote $0.7 - 0.13$ and then got confused. *"Wait,"* he said. *"Isn't 7 minus 13 negative?"* Help Mishka figure out what is going on. Did he write down the problem correctly? Why or why not?

c.   Kelly said, *"I want to subtract hundredths from hundredths and tenths from tenths. How can I subtract 3 hundredths from none? My brother did this."* She wrote the work shown at right. Help Kelly understand what her brother was doing.

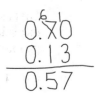

$$\begin{array}{r} 0.\overset{6}{\cancel{7}}\overset{1}{0} \\ 0.13 \\ \hline 0.57 \end{array}$$

Making Connections: Course 1

7-96.   Pedro had $3\frac{1}{4}$ cups of flour. He used $1\frac{2}{3}$ cups to make some bread and he wonders how much he has left.

   a.   Estimate how much flour he has left. Is it more or less than two cups? How can you tell?

   b.   Write an expression involving subtraction to represent the amount of flour that Pedro has left. Then subtract to find the amount of flour that remains. Was your estimate in part (a) close?

7-97.   Mishka and Kelly proposed two different methods to help Pedro calculate $3\frac{1}{4}-1\frac{2}{3}$.

   Mishka's Method: *"I will change both of these numbers to fractions greater than one."* He wrote the work below.

   Step 1: $3\frac{1}{4}-1\frac{2}{3}=\frac{13}{4}-\frac{5}{3}$

   Step 2: $\frac{13}{4}\cdot\frac{3}{3}-\frac{5}{3}\cdot\frac{4}{4}=\frac{39}{12}-\frac{20}{12}$

   Step 3: $\frac{39}{12}-\frac{20}{12}=\frac{19}{12}$

   Step 4: $\frac{19}{12}=1\frac{7}{12}$

   Kelly's Method: *"I will subtract the fractions from the fractions and the whole numbers from the whole numbers."* She wrote the work below.

   Step A: $3\frac{1}{4}\cdot\frac{3}{3} \Rightarrow 3\frac{3}{12}$
   $-1\frac{2}{3}\cdot\frac{4}{4} \Rightarrow -1\frac{8}{12}$

   Step B: $2 3\frac{12+3}{12} \Rightarrow 2\frac{15}{12}$
   $-1\frac{8}{12} \Rightarrow -1\frac{8}{12}$

   Step C: $2\frac{15}{12}$
   $-1\frac{8}{12}$
   $1\frac{7}{12}$

   Discuss Mishka and Kelly's methods with your team. For each method, **explain** what is happening in each step. Then do each of the following problems.

   a. $4\frac{4}{5}-2\frac{1}{4}$ b. $10\frac{1}{4}-3\frac{5}{7}$ c. $6\frac{1}{6}-1\frac{5}{8}$

7-98.   Nigel was adding $2\frac{5}{6}+1\frac{7}{10}$.

   a.   Estimate the size of this sum. What whole numbers should the answer lie between? **Explain**.

   b.   Work with your team to add these fractions.

   c.   How big is the sum? **Describe** where the sum is on a number line. Can you tell just by looking quickly at the number?

   d.   Write the sum as a fraction greater than one (such as $\frac{a}{b}$) and as a mixed number (such as $c\frac{d}{b}$). Which form makes it most clear how big this number is?

7-99.   Kelly needed to calculate the sum $2.4+5.9$, and she noticed that she could use a mental math strategy.

   She explained her thinking like this: *"2.4 is one tenth less than 2.5 and 5.9 is one tenth less than 6. I know that 2.5 plus 6 is 8.5. So the answer to this sum must be two tenths less than that, or 8.3."*

   Use mental math strategies to make each of the following calculations. Can you think of more than one way? Be prepared to share your strategies with your team and with the class.

   a. $1.6+4.8$ b. $4\frac{5}{7}+1\frac{3}{7}$ c. $8.1-1.6$ d. $3\frac{5}{6}-1\frac{2}{3}$

METHODS AND **M**EANINGS

MATH NOTES

Adding and Subtracting Fractions

In order to add or subtract two fractions that are written with the same denominator, you simply add or subtract the numerators. For example, $\frac{1}{5} + \frac{2}{5} = \frac{3}{5}$.

If the fractions have different denominators, rewrite them first as fractions with the same denominator (by using the Giant One, for example). Below are examples of adding and subtracting two fractions with different denominators.

Addition Example:

$$\frac{1}{5} + \frac{2}{3} \Rightarrow \frac{1}{5} \cdot \boxed{\frac{3}{3}} + \frac{2}{3} \cdot \boxed{\frac{5}{5}} \Rightarrow \frac{3}{15} + \frac{10}{15} = \frac{13}{15}$$

Subtraction Example:

$$\frac{5}{6} - \frac{1}{4} \Rightarrow \frac{5}{6} \cdot \boxed{\frac{2}{2}} - \frac{1}{4} \cdot \boxed{\frac{3}{3}} \Rightarrow \frac{10}{12} - \frac{3}{12} = \frac{7}{12}$$

Using algebra to write the general method,

$$\frac{a}{b} + \frac{c}{d} \Rightarrow \frac{a}{b} \cdot \boxed{\frac{d}{d}} + \frac{c}{d} \cdot \boxed{\frac{b}{b}} \Rightarrow \frac{a \cdot d}{b \cdot d} + \frac{b \cdot c}{b \cdot d} \Rightarrow \frac{a \cdot d + b \cdot c}{b \cdot d}$$

Review & Preview

7-100. Jane has two broken ruler segments. One shows from $1\frac{1}{2}$ to 3 inches and the other shows $3\frac{1}{4}$ to $5\frac{1}{2}$ inches. Which piece is longer? How much longer?

7-101. For each of the following sums or differences, estimate the size of the answer. In other words, tell which whole numbers the answer should be between. Then check your conclusion by calculating the sum or difference.

a. $5.2 - 2.09$ b. $25\frac{1}{3} - 17\frac{5}{6}$ c. $3\frac{3}{4} + 2\frac{5}{7}$ d. $103.57 + 29.6$

7-102. For each of the following pairs of fractions, decide which fraction is larger or whether they are equivalent. For each part, show your thinking clearly.

a. $\frac{3}{4}$ and $\frac{5}{6}$

b. $\frac{4}{9}$ and $\frac{1}{3}$

c. $\frac{3}{8}$ and $\frac{1}{3}$

7-103. Complete the web at right.

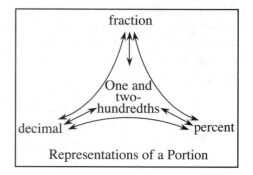

Representations of a Portion

7-104. Assume that each of the shaded tiles in the large rectangle below has an area of 1 square foot. Use this information to answer the following questions.

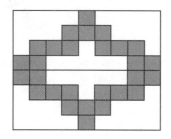

a. What is the total area of all of the shaded tiles?

b. What is the total area of the rectangle that is not shaded?

7-105. Look at the graph at right.

a. Write the coordinates (x, y) of the three points shown on the graph.

b. Write the coordinates (x, y) of two other points that would fall on the same line as the three points shown.

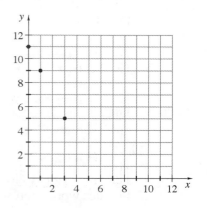

7.3.2 How can I calculate it?

A Culminating Challenge

People throughout history have enjoyed solving puzzles as hobbies. Today you and your team will work together to decipher clues that will point you in the direction of a hidden treasure. It is important that your team members are communicating and in agreement on the puzzle so you reach the treasure successfully. As you work today, keep the following questions in mind:

How can we use this information?

How can we convince others that it is true?

7-106. TRAIL TO THE TREASURE OF TRAGON

The Treasure of Tragon lies somewhere in the wilderness around the ruins of the ancient city of Tragon. The two scrolls below have been discovered and hold the clues you need to find the treasure! Archeologists have figured out that ■ represents 1 mile on the map.

Your task: Obtain a map of the region (on the Lesson 7.3.2 Resource Page) from your teacher. With your team, use the clues below to decipher the message and draw the correct path on your map. Notice that your starting point is clearly marked on the resource page. Your teacher will use a secret map to check your progress periodically. Be careful not to get lost in the Monstrous Mountains, fall into Crocodile Creek, wander into the Lion's Lair, or sink into the Slithery Sands!

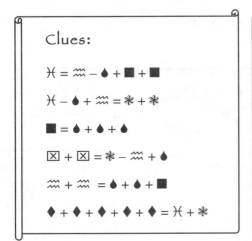

7-107.   Using the same values for the symbols in problem 7-106, find another set of
         directions that will also get you to the treasure. (While you can just modify the
         current directions so that you take the same path, you can also make a new
         path.) Remember that your path should not run into any obstacles!

Mᴇᴛʜᴏᴅs ᴀɴᴅ Mᴇᴀɴɪɴɢs

Adding and Subtracting Mixed Numbers

To add or subtract mixed numbers, you can either add or
subtract their parts, or you can change the mixed numbers into
fractions greater than one.

To add or subtract mixed numbers by
adding or subtracting their parts, add the
whole number parts and the fraction
parts separately. Adjust if the fraction
in the answer would be greater than one
or less than zero. For example, the sum
of $3\frac{4}{5}+1\frac{2}{3}$ is calculated at right.

$$3\frac{4}{5} = 3+\frac{4}{5} \cdot \frac{3}{3} = 3\frac{12}{15}$$
$$+1\frac{2}{3} = 1+\frac{2}{3} \cdot \frac{5}{5} = +1\frac{10}{15}$$
$$4\frac{22}{15} = 5\frac{7}{15}$$

It is also possible to add or subtract
mixed numbers by changing them into
fractions greater than one and then
adding or subtracting as with fractions
between zero and one. For example, the
sum of $2\frac{1}{6}+1\frac{4}{5}$ is calculated at right.

$$2\frac{1}{6}+1\frac{4}{5} = \frac{13}{6}+\frac{9}{5}$$
$$= \frac{13}{6} \cdot \frac{5}{5} + \frac{9}{5} \cdot \frac{6}{6}$$
$$= \frac{65}{30} + \frac{54}{30}$$
$$= \frac{119}{30}$$
$$= 3\frac{29}{30}$$

Review & Preview

7-108.   Calculate each of the following expressions. Simplify each of your answers as
         much as possible and write any answers greater than one as mixed numbers.

a. $\frac{3}{5}+\frac{1}{4}$ b. $\frac{3}{4}-\frac{2}{3}$ c. $5\frac{1}{2}+4\frac{1}{3}$ d. $\frac{7}{8} \cdot \frac{5}{6}$

Making Connections: Course 1

7-109. Alan collects rocks. He weighs them before he puts them in piles in his backyard. In the last two weeks, he has recorded the following weights: 32, 47, 25, 27, 36, 75, 40, 41, 33, 35, 32, 32, 28, and 75.

   a. Make a stem-and-leaf plot to help him organize the information so that he can get a better idea of how hard he is working.

   b. Find the mean, median, and mode for the information.

   c. Which measure of central tendency was most affected by the outlier of 75 pounds?

7-110. Mary is taking advantage of the 20% off sale at Cassie's Cashew Shoppe and wants to figure out how much she will save on a purchase of $65. She drew the percent ruler shown at right. Copy the ruler onto your paper and help her figure out what 20% of $65 is.

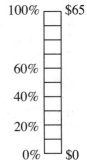

7-111. John and Dave are building a rectangular pen next to the barn for their goat, Ginny. They plan to use one 60-foot wall of the barn as part of the pen, so they only need to build the remaining three sides. They want the width of the pen to be half of the length. How much fencing will they need to complete Ginny's pen? Can you find more than one answer?

7-112. Copy and complete each of the Diamond Problems below. The pattern used in the Diamond Problems is shown at right.

a.

b.

c.

d.

Chapter 7 Closure What have I learned?

Reflection and Synthesis

The activities below offer you a chance to reflect upon what you have learned during this chapter. As you work, look for concepts that you feel very comfortable with, ideas that you would like to learn more about, and topics you need more help with. Look for **connections** between ideas as well as **connections** with material that you learned previously.

①   SUMMARIZING MY UNDERSTANDING

This activity will give you an opportunity to show what you know about one of the most important concepts in this course. Your teacher may give you a graphic organizer on which to display and **explain** your ideas.

Particular Parts

The idea of counting parts that are alike is a fundamental aspect of much of the mathematics in this course as well as in future math courses and the real world outside of math class.

Your task:

- Work with your team to brainstorm ideas for responses to the two sentence starters below that contain the phrase "counting like parts" (or very similar wording). Think about situations that you have encountered in this course.

- Write your own response to each sentence starter on your own paper. For each response, include examples that demonstrate your thinking.

- Finally, create your own sentence starter and a response to it that also includes the phrase "counting like parts." Again, remember to include examples to clearly show your thinking.

Sentence starter 1: When I measure length, I…

Sentence starter 2: When I think about the connections between adding decimals and fractions, I…

Sentence starter 3: Make and respond to your own sentence starter.

Working the problems in this section will help you to evaluate which types of problems that you feel comfortable with and which you need more help with.

Solve each problem as completely as you can. The table at the end of this closure section provides answers to these problems. It also tells you where you can find additional help and practice on problems like these.

CL 7-113. Which fraction is larger, $\frac{5}{8}$ or $\frac{5}{12}$? **Explain** how you know.

CL 7-114. Simplify the following expressions without a calculator.

a. $\frac{3}{7} + \frac{2}{7}$ b. $\frac{1}{2} - \frac{1}{8}$ c. $\frac{5}{11} \cdot 2$ d. $\frac{4 + 3 \cdot 10}{2}$

CL 7-115. Consider the rectangle at right.

a. Find the area of the rectangle.

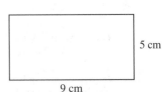

b. The above rectangle is the base of the right prism shown below. Find the volume of this prism.

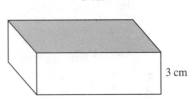

CL 7-116. Minneapolis received $1\frac{5}{6}$ feet of snow in December, and in January $2\frac{1}{5}$ feet of snow fell there. Without a calculator, determine how many feet of snow Minneapolis received in those two months. Write your answer as a mixed number.

CL 7-117. Determine which of the following fractions are equivalent. Show how you know.

$$\frac{6}{14}, \quad \frac{2}{9}, \quad \frac{15}{35}, \quad \frac{4}{10}, \quad \frac{12}{54}$$

CL 7-118. The larger triangle shown below is an enlargement of the smaller triangle. Find the missing length marked n.

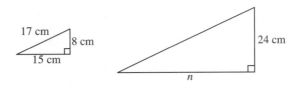

CL 7-119. Franco has 46 rock songs, 18 jazz tunes, and 16 classical pieces on his MP3 player. If his MP3 player is on random shuffle mode, find the probability it will play the following music. Write each probability as a fraction, decimal, and percent.

a. Classical

b. Not jazz

CL 7-120. For each of the problems above, do the following:

- Draw a bar or number line that represents 0 to 10.

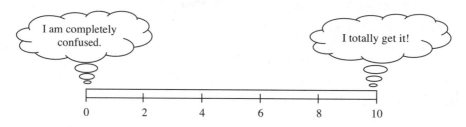

- Color or shade in a portion of the bar that represents your level of understanding and comfort with completing that problem on your own.

If any of your bars are less than a 5, choose *one* of those problems and do one of the following tasks:

- Write two questions that you would like to ask about that problem.
- Brainstorm two things that you DO know about that type of problem.

If all of your bars are at 5 or above, choose one problem and do one of these tasks:

- Write two questions that you might ask or hints that you might give to a student that was stuck on the problem.
- Make a new problem that is similar and more challenging than that problem and solve it.

③ SUPPORTING MY UNDERSTANDING

You have several tools and references available to help support your learning – your teacher, your study team, your math book, and your Toolkit to name only a few. At the end of each chapter, you will have an opportunity to review your Toolkit for completeness as well as to revise or update your Toolkit to better reflect your current understanding of big ideas.

The main elements of your Toolkit should be your Learning Log, Math Notes and the vocabulary used in this chapter. Math words that are new to this chapter appear in bold in the text. Refer to the lists provided below and follow your teacher's instructions to revise your Toolkit, which will help make it a useful reference for you as you complete this chapter and prepare to begin the next one.

Learning Log Entries
- Lesson 7.1.2 – Volume of Prisms
- Lesson 7.2.3 – Converting Fractions to Decimals and Percents
- Lesson 7.2.5 – Adding and Subtracting Fractions

Math Notes
- Lesson 7.2.1 – Volume of Right Prisms
- Lesson 7.2.3 – Dividing Decimals by Integers
- Lesson 7.3.1 – Adding and Subtracting Fractions
- Lesson 7.3.2 – Adding and Subtracting Mixed Numbers

Mathematical Vocabulary

The following is a list of vocabulary found in this chapter. Some of the words have been seen in the previous chapter. The words in bold are the words that are new to this chapter. Make sure that you are familiar with the terms below and that you know what they mean. For the words that you do not know, refer to the glossary or index. You might also add these words to your Toolkit so that you can reference them in the future.

common denominator	**cubic units**
dimension	**greatest common factor**
lateral surfaces	**lowest common denominator**
one-dimensional	**right rectangular prisms**
surface area	**three-dimensional**
two-dimensional	**volume**

Process Words

compare	connect	convince
describe	estimate	evaluate
explain	investigate	organize
predict	represent	simplify

Answers and Support for Closure Activity #2
Assessing My Understanding

Problem	Solution	Need Help?	More Practice
CL 7-113.	$\frac{5}{8}$, explanations vary. Sample explanation: $\frac{5}{8}$ is larger than $\frac{5}{12}$ because when the two fractions are compared in like terms, $\frac{5}{8} = \frac{15}{24}$ and $\frac{5}{12} = \frac{10}{24}$, $\frac{15}{24} > \frac{10}{24}$.	Lessons 7.2.1 and 7.2.4	Problems 7-29, 7-53, and 7-102
CL 7-114.	a. $\frac{5}{7}$ b. $\frac{1}{2} - \frac{1}{8} = \frac{4}{8} - \frac{1}{8} = \frac{3}{8}$ c. $\frac{5}{11} \cdot 2 = \frac{5}{11} \cdot \frac{2}{1} = \frac{10}{11}$ d. $\frac{4+3\cdot10}{2} = \frac{4+30}{2} = \frac{34}{2} = 17$	Lessons 7.2.2, 7.2.4, and 7.2.5 Math Notes box in Lesson 7.3.1 Learning Log (problem 7-87)	Problems 7-37, 7-43, 7-70, 7-72, 7-74, 7-81, 7-86, 7-90, and 7-108
CL 7-115.	a. 45 sq cm b. 135 cu cm	Lessons 7.1.1 and 7.1.2 Math Notes box in Lesson 7.2.1 Learning Log (problem 7-19)	Problems 7-5, 7-17, 7-20, and 7-80
CL 7-116.	$1\frac{5}{6} + 2\frac{1}{5} = \frac{55}{30} + \frac{66}{30} = \frac{121}{30} = 4\frac{1}{30}$	Lessons 7.2.2, 7.2.4, and 7.3.1 Math Notes box in Lesson 7.3.2	Problems 7-96 through 7-101
CL 7-117.	$\frac{2}{9}$ and $\frac{12}{54}$ are equivalent; $\frac{6}{14}$ and $\frac{15}{35}$ are equivalent. Explanations vary; sample explanation: by reducing all of the fractions into lowest terms, it is easy to determine which are equivalent: $\frac{6}{14} = \frac{3}{7}$; $\frac{2}{9}$ is already reduced into lowest terms; $\frac{15}{35} = \frac{3}{7}$; $\frac{4}{10} = \frac{2}{5}$; $\frac{12}{54} = \frac{2}{9}$.	Lessons 7.2.1, 7.2.3, and 7.2.4	Problems 7-51, 7-55, 7-65, 7-77, and 7-102

Problem	Solution	Need Help?	More Practice
CL 7-118.	$n = 45$ cm	Lessons 6.1.3, 6.1.4, and 6.3.1 Math Notes box in Lesson 6.1.3 Learning Log (problems 6-12, 6-24, and 6-121)	Problems 6-106, 6-118, and 6-119
CL 7-119.	a. $P = \frac{16}{80} = \frac{1}{5} = 0.2 = 20\%$ b. $P = \frac{62}{80} = \frac{31}{40} = 0.775 = 77.5\%$	Lessons 5.2.1 and 5.2.2 Math Notes boxes in Lessons 5.2.2 and 5.2.4 Learning Log (problems 5-37 and 5-52)	Problems 5-51, 5-55, 5-64, 5-73, and CL 5-89

Variables and Dividing Portions

CHAPTER 8   Variables and Dividing Portions

You will start this chapter by studying patterns and looking for **multiple ways** to see and describe them. You will use your observations about patterns to make predictions and to generalize, and you will see how variables and graphs can help to do this.

As you did in Chapter 2, you will represent unknown quantities with variables, and you will use what you know about a problem to find the value of these variables. You will learn to use known ideas about angles to find the measure of other angles.

In this chapter, you will learn how to:

➤ Describe a pattern in several ways.

➤ Use a variable to generalize and to represent unknown quantities.

➤ Write multiple expressions to describe a pattern and recognize whether the expressions are equivalent.

➤ Find the value of a variable expression when the value of the variable is known.

➤ Find the solution to equations describing certain situations.

➤ Use graphs to represent all pairs of numbers that make a certain rule true.

➤ Divide with fractions, mixed numbers, and decimals.

Guiding Questions

Think about these questions throughout this chapter:

How can I describe the pattern?

How can I represent it?

How can I use a variable?

What are expressions and equations?

Does it make sense?

Chapter Outline

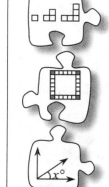

Section 8.1   In this section, you will learn how to describe patterns. In addition, you will look at one pattern in several different ways and learn how to extend it.

Section 8.2   Using a picture frame situation, you will write **expressions** with **variables** and learn about equivalent expressions. You will use graphs to organize expressions for different values, as well as learn to make graphs that represent all of the points that make a rule true.

Section 8.3   You will use variables in new contexts: as unknown lengths, ages, and angle measures. You will also learn some principles of angle relationships, including relationships of angles within a triangle, and you will use these ideas to find unknown angle measures.

Section 8.4   You will extend your understanding of operations with fractions and decimals to include division.

Making Connections: Course 1

8.1.1 How can I describe the pattern?

Describing and Extending Patterns

Patterns are fundamental to the study of mathematics. Indeed, they are fundamental to humans' ability to understand our world. In the very beginning of this course, you looked at a pattern and worked on finding ways to describe it. In this chapter, you will study patterns and learn about using algebra to describe them and to make predictions. As you work with your team in this lesson, keep the following questions in mind.

Is there another way to see or describe the pattern?

How is it growing?

How can we explain our thinking?

8-1. TAMARA'S PATTERN – Pattern #1

Tamara was looking at the pattern that you investigated in Lesson 1.1.3 and wondered what would happen if she made it grow in a different way. So she created the pattern shown at right.

Figure 1   Figure 2   Figure 3

a. Copy Tamara's new dot pattern on graph paper. What should the 4th and 5th figures look like? Draw them on your paper.

b. How can you describe the way the pattern is growing?

c. How many dots would be in the 12th figure of the pattern? What would it look like? Describe the figure.

d. How many dots would be in the 30th figure? How can you describe the figure *without* drawing it? Can you describe it with words, numbers and a diagram? Be ready to **explain** your ideas to the class.

8-2.   PATTERN MANIA – Pattern #2

Tamara decided to change the pattern
again by connecting the dots with
toothpicks, as shown at right.

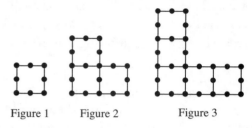

Figure 1   Figure 2   Figure 3

a. Discuss what you see with your
    team. What do you notice?
    How do the toothpicks change the
    pattern? How can you describe
    how this new pattern is growing?

b. Assuming that the pattern keeps growing in the way that you described in
    part (a), draw the 4th and 5th figures in the pattern.

c. How many toothpicks would be in the 12th figure of the pattern? What
    about the 30th figure? Are these answers different for the toothpick pattern
    than from the dot pattern? Why or why not? Be prepared to **explain** your
    thinking to the class.

8-3.   Analyze each of the patterns – Patterns #3, #4, and #5 – in parts (a) through (c)
        below by addressing each of the following points.

- Draw figures 1 through 5 on your own paper.

- How can you describe the way the pattern is growing?

- How many toothpicks or tiles would be in the 12th figure of the pattern?
  What would it look like? Draw it.

- How many toothpicks or tiles would be in the 30th figure? How can you
  describe the figure *without* drawing it? Can you describe it with words,
  numbers and a diagram?

a. Pattern #3 is a pattern of
    frames built with square tiles,
    as shown at right.

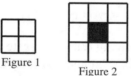

Figure 1

Figure 2

Figure 3

b. Pattern #4 is a pattern of triangles
    built with toothpicks, as shown at
    right.

Figure 1   Figure 2   Figure 3

Problem continues on next page →

8-3.   *Problem continued from previous page.*

c. Pattern #5 is a pattern of big "H's" built with toothpicks as shown at right.

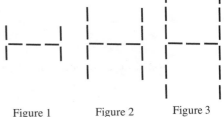

Figure 1   Figure 2   Figure 3

8-4.   For the pattern(s) assigned by your teacher, prepare a brief presentation that contains the following information.

- **Descriptions** of each way that your team saw the pattern and its growth. The **more ways** to see it, the better!

- Your strategies for figuring out how many toothpicks, dots, or tiles should be in the 12th and 30th figures. Be sure to **explain** your thinking clearly.

8-5.   PATTERN MANIA REVISITED

With your team, revisit the patterns in problem 8-3 and answer the questions below for each one.

a. Does the pattern have a figure that contains exactly 200 toothpicks, dots, or tiles? What about 303 toothpicks, dots, or tiles? If so, which figures? How can you tell? If not, **explain** how you know.

b. So far in this lesson, you have extended patterns to larger figures. Now think about reversing this process and imagine the pattern getting smaller. The figure that would come before Figure 1 would be Figure 0. Which of them would have a Figure 0? What would Figure 0 look like? Discuss this with your team and then draw Figure 0 for each pattern that has one on your own paper.

8-6.   Work with your team to create another pattern that grows by the same number of toothpicks for each figure. Draw the first, second and third figures of your pattern. Does your new pattern contain a figure with exactly 200 toothpicks? What about 303 toothpicks? Does your pattern have a Figure 0? If so, draw it. Again, **explain** how you know.

8-7.   Jesse created a pattern that has exactly 8 tiles in each figure. In other words, it grows by 0 tiles each time! How could his pattern look? Discuss this with your team and draw two different possibilities for Jesse's pattern.

8-8.   The pattern below changes by adding two tiles for each new figure. Use Figure 5 to answer the following questions.

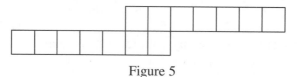

Figure 5

a.   How many tiles would be in Figure 7? How do you know?

b.   What could Figure 3 look like? Sketch one possibility.

c.   Could there be a Figure 0? If so, how many tiles would it have?

d.   If the pattern continues, will there be a figure with exactly 24 tiles? **Explain** your answer with a sentence *or* a drawing.

8-9.   Calculate the volume of a prism that is 5 cm high with a base that has an area of 34 square cm. Sketch what this prism could look like.

8-10.   Jane has two broken ruler segments. One shows from $1\frac{1}{2}$ to 3 inches and the other shows $3\frac{1}{4}$ to $5\frac{1}{2}$ inches. Which piece is longer? How much longer?

8-11.   On grid paper, draw a rectangle with a width of 4 units and a length of 5 units. If you were to enlarge your rectangle so that the new length is 12 units, how wide would it be? Show how you know.

8-12.   What shape has the following characteristics? Is there more than one possibility? Draw an example of each of the possible shapes.

- The shape is **equilateral**, that is, all sides are the same length.

- The angles are all **acute**, that is, smaller than 90°.

- The shape has fewer than 5 sides.

8-13.   Ms. Tormoehlen loves to shop and now has a closet full of beautiful shirts. In her closet are 6 blue, 4 red, 8 brown, and 3 white shirts. Her electricity went out during a storm and she needs to pick a shirt in the dark. Find the probability that the shirt she selects is:

    a. Red or blue   b. Not red   c. Green

8-14.   Study the dot pattern at right.

    a. Draw the 3rd and 5th figures.

Fig. 1   Fig. 2   Fig. 3   Fig. 4   Fig. 5

    b. How many dots will there be in the 50th figure?

    c. Is there a figure that will have exactly 38 dots? If there is, which figure is it?

8-15.   Compute each sum or difference.

    a. $\frac{2}{3}+\frac{1}{5}$ b. $\frac{7}{8}-\frac{1}{4}$ c. $1\frac{2}{3}+3\frac{1}{4}$ d. $7-3\frac{2}{5}$

8-16.   Multiply the following numbers without using a calculator.

    a. $\frac{7}{8}\cdot\frac{5}{6}$ b. $(3.1)(0.02)$ c. $1\frac{3}{5}\cdot 2\frac{1}{3}$ d. $\frac{2}{3}\cdot\frac{20}{7}$

8-17.   **Explain** how you can convert $\frac{5}{4}$ to a percent. Then write $\frac{5}{4}$ as a percent.

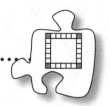

Comparing Strategies for Counting

In this lesson, you will look at one of the patterns from yesterday and work with your team to find different ways to determine the number of tiles in the figure. Then you will see if these methods will still work when the size of the figure is changed.

Consider the following questions in your discussion.

How do we see it?

How can we **explain** our thinking?

8-18.   One figure of the square tile frame pattern from
Lesson 8.1.1 is shown at right. *Without* talking to your
teammates or counting one by one, find the number of
tiles in the frame *mentally*. Be ready to share your
method and how you see it with your team and with
the class.

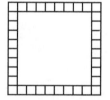

a.   When everyone in your team is ready, share your methods one at a time.
Be sure to **explain** to your teammates how your steps or process connect
back to the drawing itself.

b.   Pam told her team that when she first looked at the figure she thought that
there were 40 tiles in the frame. **Explain** how Pam might have been
looking at the drawing to see this answer and what she might have
overlooked.

c.   Your teacher will now ask teams to share the methods that they discussed.
Record and color-code each method on the Lesson 8.2.1 Resource Page in
the manner demonstrated by your teacher on the board or overhead as each
one is presented.

8-19.   Here are some methods that students from another class used to find the number of tiles in problem 8-18. Which ones are like the ones that students in your class came up with? Which ones are new or different? If there are new methods, describe how that student might have been seeing the picture frame to come up with that method. Then add any new strategies to your resource page.

- Jonas' Method: $4 \cdot 10 - 4$

- Curran's Method: $10 + 9 + 9 + 8$

- Tina's Method: $10 + 10 + 8 + 8$

- Ramond's Method: $10 \cdot 10 - 8 \cdot 8$

- Alyssa's Method: $9 \cdot 4$

- TJ's Method: $4 \cdot 8 + 4$

8-20.   Now imagine that the frame from problem 8-18 has been shrunk so that it is 6 tiles by 6 tiles. With your team, consider the following questions *without drawing* the frame.

a.   Choose one of the methods for counting the tiles and use it to find the number of tiles in that square's frame.

b.   Choose another method and use it to find the number of tiles in the 6 by 6 frame. Did you get the same answer using both methods? Should you?

8-21.   Now imagine that the frame has been enlarged to be 100 tiles by 100 tiles. Choose two counting methods and use them both to find the number of tiles in the frame. Did you get the same answer using both methods? Should you?

8-22.   Examine the figure formed by square tiles at right. How can you find out how many small squares there are in this diagram *without* counting each one? Consider this as you answer the questions below.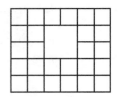

a.   Create and solve an **addition** problem to show how many squares there are.

b.   Create a **subtraction** problem to find out how may squares there are.

8-23. A team of students worked on problem 8-18. Their work is shown below. Unfortunately, the expressions, descriptions, and diagrams got mixed up! Match the counting method, word description, and corresponding diagram that describe the same strategy.

Counting Methods	Word Descriptions	Diagrams
a. $4 \cdot 10 - 4$	1. Start in one corner and count 9 four times around the picture frame.	A.
b. $10 + 9 + 9 + 8$	2. Take a side length of 10 four times and take away the 4 corners.	B.
c. $9 \cdot 4$	3. Take the entire 100's grid and subtract the inside part of the picture frame.	C.
d. $(10 \cdot 10) - (8 \cdot 8)$	4. Take the top length, then add the two vertical sides and add the bottom.	D.

8-24. Miranda is a wonderful Shape Designer. Below are some of the orders she has received. For each order draw at least two different shapes that fit the description.

a. An acute triangle that is also an isosceles triangle.

b. A shape with two obtuse angles and four sides.

c. A pentagon with at least one acute and one obtuse angle.

8-25. Multiple Choice: The sum $\frac{7}{16} + \frac{3}{5} + \frac{4}{7} + \frac{3}{7}$ is approximately equal to which of the following whole numbers? **Explain** how you know.

A. 1   B. 2   C. 3   D. 4

Making Connections: Course 1

8-26. Riley was monitoring the growth of his favorite tomato plant and he collected the data in the table at right.

Time (days)	Height (cm)
10	3
14	4.3
18	7
21	8.9
23	11.4

a. Graph Riley's data.

b. What can you tell Riley about his plant based on the data?

$8.2.2$ How can I describe *any* figure?

Using Variables to Generalize

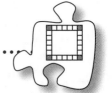

In this lesson, you will look more closely at the methods you developed in Lesson 8.2.1 to find the number of tiles in a square frame. You will work with your team to generalize the strategies to describe the number of tiles in a square frame of *any* size.

8-27. One method to find the number of tiles in the frame of a 10 by 10 square can be represented by the diagram at right.

a. Look at your Lesson 8.2.1 Resource Page. Whose method was this?

b. Use this method to determine the number of tiles in the frame of a square that is 18 tiles by 18 tiles.

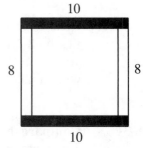

8-28. GENERALIZING

Can you describe how to use this method to find the number of tiles in a square frame with *any* side length?

Your task: Work with your team to write a general set of directions in *words* that describe how to calculate the number of tiles in the frame of any square, if you are given the side length.

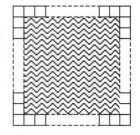

Discussion Points

What do we need to know to begin the calculation?

What operations or steps do we need to do?

What parts of the process change when the size of the square changes? What parts stay the same?

8-29.   What if you wanted to send the directions from problem 8-28 in a text message? When people send text messages often they find ways to shorten words. For example, they might use letters that sound like the word, such as "u" instead of "you" or they might use abbreviations such as "btw" instead of "by the way." It is important, however, that the person reading the text message understands the abbreviations the sender uses or the message will not make any sense to them.

In Lesson 2.4.1 you used a **variable** to represent an unknown quantity such as Cecil's leap. In that case, your variable letter stood for a specific amount that you did not know. Now you are going to use a variable in a different way – to represent a part of a general relationship or rule.

Your task: You have written a set of directions for calculating the number of tiles in any square frame. Now, how can you use numbers and symbols to shorten your directions? With your team find a way to shorten your set of directions by using a **variable** (such as x) to stand for "the number of tiles in one side of the frame."

8-30.   Refer to your Lesson 8.2.1 Resource Page. Choose a different method from Lesson 8.2.1 for finding the number of tiles in any square frame. Work with your team to shorten this method into an **algebraic expression** (an expression with numbers and symbols). Be prepared to share your ideas with the class.

8-31.   **Compare** the two expressions that you have created in problems 8-29 and 8-30. The expressions represent the number of tiles in a square frame of any side length, which we know for a given side length must result in the same amount. For example, for a 10 by 10 frame, the answer is 36; for both expressions to "work" we should get this answer.

a.   How can we check that your two expressions are equivalent, that is, that they might look different, but are the same as one another?

b.   Jerrold came up with the following expressions. Are they equivalent? How can you tell?

$$2x + 2 \qquad\qquad x + 1 + x + 1 \qquad\qquad 2(x+1)$$

Making Connections: Course 1

METHODS AND MEANINGS

Describing Growth Patterns

The growth in patterns may be **visualized** in various ways. By understanding how a figure grows, you can then predict how the pattern will continue (assuming it continues to grow the same way). Patterns can usually be seen in several different ways. For the dot pattern at right, two different ways of **describing** the pattern are given.

Figure 1   Figure 2   Figure 3

Method 1: Figure 1 is one row by two columns, Figure 2 is two rows by three columns, and Figure 3 is three rows by four columns. So, Figure 4 will be four rows by five columns (20 dots) and Figure 5 will be five rows by six columns (30 dots).

Method 2: Figure 1 is a one by one array of dots plus a single dot to the right, Figure 2 is a two by two square array of dots plus a column of two dots. Figure 3 is a three by three square array of dots plus a column of three dots. So, Figure 4 will have $4^2 + 4 = 20$ dots and Figure 5 will have $5^2 + 5 = 30$ dots.

8-32.   Draw a rectangle with an area of 52 square units and whole number dimensions.

a.   Find the perimeter of your rectangle. Label the length and width on your drawing.

b.   Is there only one rectangle that you can draw? If not, draw another rectangle and find the perimeter, length, and width.

8-33.   Arrange these numbers from least to greatest.

$$\frac{3}{5}, \ \frac{7}{3}, \ -\frac{3}{4}, \ 1\frac{2}{5}, \ -\frac{1}{4}$$

8-34.   Multiply and simplify your results.

a. $\frac{1}{4} \cdot 4$ b. $\frac{7}{8} \cdot \frac{8}{7}$ c. $2\frac{2}{3} \cdot \frac{3}{8}$

d.   What was the product of the two numbers in each part above?

When two numbers have a product of one they are called **reciprocals** or **multiplicative inverses**. What is the reciprocal or multiplicative inverse of each of these numbers?

e. $\frac{2}{3}$ f.   7   g. $4\frac{1}{3}$

8-35.   *Tires R Us* is having a 30% off sale. Use a percent ruler to find your savings on a tire that regularly costs $45.

8-36.   **Describe** how each of the following multipliers would change a photograph.

a. $\frac{19}{20}$ b. $\frac{1}{30}$ c. $\frac{16}{16}$ d. $\frac{21}{17}$

8.2.3 How can a graph help?

Using Graphs to Study Patterns

In Lesson 8.1.1, you looked at patterns and considered whether they would ever have a specific number of dots, tiles or toothpicks (such as 200 or 303). You were also asked to find the number of tiles in a specific figure number, such as Figure 30. In this lesson, you will return to these types of questions, only you will use a graph to help organize the information and apply your new understanding of variables and expressions. You and your class will see an example of the power of graphing and algebra!

8-37.   Bonnie, the owner of the "I've Been Framed!" picture framing shop, is very excited about the pattern that you have described about the number of tiles in different sizes of square frames. She knows there are several different expressions she can use to **describe** this pattern, two of which are $x + x + (x - 2) + (x - 2)$ and $4x - 4$ (where x  represents the number of tiles on a side of the frame). She would like a way that she can see the side length and total number of tiles for *lots* of different frames all at once, so she has asked you to make a graph for her.

a.   How could a graph be useful for Bonnie? Discuss your ideas with your team and be prepared to share them with the class.

b.   The smallest square frame that Bonnie can make has a side length of 3 tiles, and the largest frame she can currently make has a side length of 20 tiles.

- Obtain copies of the Lesson 8.2.3 Resource Page for each member of your team.

- Choose three possible side lengths and calculate the total number of tiles each frame would contain.

- Add this information to the table on the Lesson 8.2.3 Resource Page, fill in the missing information about scale on the graph, and plot one point for each frame on the axes provided.

c.   Share your numbers with those of other teams. Add information to your list until you have at least 7 pairs of numbers and 7 points on your graph.

d.   Does it **make sense** for Bonnie to include a point for a frame with a side that is 4.5 tiles long? Why or why not?

e.   How can you tell from your graph (without making any new calculations) where points would go for *all* of her possible frames? Discuss this with your team and then complete your graph.

8-38.   Use your graph to help Bonnie with each of the following orders. Be prepared
         to **explain** how you can see each answer in your graph.

   a.   A customer wants a frame that has 8 tiles along each side. How many tiles
         will Bonnie need for the whole frame?

   b.   Bonnie's neighbor wants a frame that is 16 tiles along each side. How
         many tiles will she need?

   c.   Bonnie's father has 32 tiles that he wants to use to frame an old photograph.
         He needs to know the dimensions of the frame so that he have the photo
         printed at the correct size. What should Bonnie tell him?

   d.   Bonnie has a set of 40 tiles that she bought while traveling in South Africa.
         What is the biggest frame size (on each side) that she can make with these
         tiles? Will she use all of her tiles?

8-39.   Bonnie has recently remodeled and she can now make larger frames. She has
         just received an order for a square frame that has 102 tiles along each side.
         How many tiles will she need in order to make this frame? **Explain** how you
         arrived at your answer. Was your graph useful?

8-40.   Bonnie has been hired to make a frame to go around a large mural. She will
         have 300 tiles to use. How many tiles should she place along one side of the
         square frame for the mural? Work with your team and be prepared to **describe**
         your process to the rest of the class.

8-41.   When you determine the number of tiles needed to make a given frame size,
         you could use the algebraic expression and change the variable from
         representing "any number" to representing a "specific number" by replacing the
         variable with the number and calculating the value of the expression for that
         value of the variable. This process is also called **evaluating** the expression for a
         specific value.

         Evaluate the following algebraic expressions for the given value of the variable.

   a. $2x + 6$ for $x = 3$ b. $5 - 3r + 2$ for $r = 8$

   c. $4(t - 3)$ for $t = 5$ d. $4c - 12$ for $c = 5$

8-42.   Bonnie's employees, Parker and Barrow, were trying to find the
         total number of tiles needed for a frame that had 24 tiles along a
         side. Parker decided to evaluate the expression $4x - 4$ for $x = 24$
         and came up with 420 tiles. From the graph that you made in
         problem 8-37, Barrow could tell that Parker's answer was wrong.
         How? What mistake do you think Parker might have made?

8-43.   When Bonnie was traveling in Bolivia, she bought 52 beautiful tiles, but when
         she arrived back at the shop, 10 of them had broken. Can Bonnie make a square
         frame that uses all of the remaining unbroken tiles? If so, how long will the
         sides be? If not, what size frame could she build to use as many of her new tiles
         as possible?

8-44.   The staff of "I've Been Framed!" has decided
         to offer a new style of picture frames. The
         length of these rectangular frames will be
         five squares longer than the width. One
         example of this type of frame is shown at
         right.

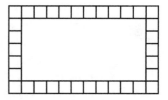

   a.   How many squares make up the example frame above? Find two different
         ways to count.

   b.   If the shorter side of a frame in this pattern is 10 squares long, how long is
         the longer side? How do you know?

   c.   If the length of the shorter side is x, **explain** how $x + x + (x + 3) + (x + 3)$ can
         represent the number of tiles in the frame.

   d.   Show that the above expression works to find the number of tiles in a
         rectangular frame with a short side length of 7.

   e.   Draw a diagram on your paper of one rectangle in this pattern. Show with
         arrows and colors how each part of the algebraic expression is related to the
         figure.

   f.   Could this type of frame ever be made of exactly 62 tiles? **Describe** how
         you found your answer.

ETHODS AND MEANINGS

Using a Variable to Generalize

We use **variables to generalize** patterns from a few specific numbers to all numbers.

For example, if a square item with whole number dimensions is surrounded by one by one tiles, how many tiles are needed? It helps to look at a specific size square first.

The outside square at right has side length 7. **One way to see** the total number of tiles needed for the frame is that it needs 7 tiles for each of the top and bottom sides and $7 - 2 = 5$ tiles for the left and right sides, as shown in the diagram above left. The total number of tiles needed for the frame can be counted as $7 + 7 + 5 + 5 = 24$.

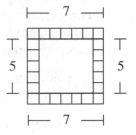

Square frames with different measures will follow the same pattern, so we can generalize by writing an expression for any side length, denoted by x. The diagram at right shows that the top and bottom each contain x tiles, and the right and left sides each contain $x - 2$ tiles, for a total number of $x + x + (x - 2) + (x - 2)$ tiles.

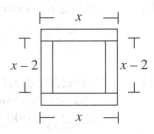

Another way to count the number of tiles in the same frame and the variable expression associated with it are shown below. Notice that the expression resulting from this counting method could be written $(x - 1) + (x - 1) + (x - 1) + (x - 1)$ or $4(x - 1)$.

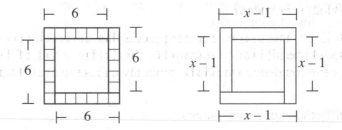

8-45.   Estimate the measure of each angle below.

a.   b.

8-46.   Evaluate the expressions below for the given values of the variables.

a. $6j - 3$ for $j = 4$.   b. $\frac{1}{2}b + 5$ for $b = 14$.

c. $8 + 4k$ for $k = 3.5$.

8-47.   The table at right shows the number of pages read and the score on the last test in Ms. Ferguson's reading class. On your own graph paper, set up axes, decide on a scale, and graph the data.

a.   Does there seem to be any **connection** between the number of pages read and the test score? **Explain.**

b.   Do any points appear to represent outliers? **Explain.**

Pages read	% on test
160	53%
280	72%
605	94%
200	75%
252	65%
565	35%
60	15%
450	90%
505	80%

8-48.   Find each sum or difference without a calculator.

a. $\frac{7}{10} + \frac{2}{3}$ b. $0.9 - 0.04$ c. $3\frac{1}{4} + 2\frac{11}{12}$ d. $14\frac{1}{3} - 9\frac{1}{5}$

8-49.   To find her usual bedtime, Zoe kept a record of what time she went to bed. These are the times she recorded: 9:30 p.m., 10:30 p.m., 10:00 p.m., 9:00 p.m., 11:00 p.m., 9:00 p.m., 9:30 p.m., 10:00 p.m., 11:00 p.m., and 9:00 p.m.

a.   What is the mode of Zoe's bedtimes?

b.   What is the median?

c.   When you calculate the mean, what values will you use for 9:30 p.m. and 10:30 p.m.?

d.   What is the mean?

e.   If Zoe wants to convince her parents that she usually goes to bed early and should be allowed to stay up late this Friday, which of these measures of central tendency would she probably choose to use? **Explain.**

8-50.   Simplify the expressions below.

a. $4 \cdot 4 + 4(5 - 2) + 7$ b. $7 - 9 \div 9 + 4(4 - 3) - 7$

8.2.4 What can a graph tell me?

Four Quadrant Graphing

In the previous lesson, you graphed the relationship between the side length of a square picture frame and the total number of tiles in that frame. In this lesson, you will develop strategies for making graphs that represent all of the pairs of numbers that make an expression with two variables equal to a particular number.

8-51.   EQUIVALENCE CHALLENGE

In Chapters 6 and 7 you worked with and created equivalent ratios and fractions. How many equivalent fractions or ratios can your team find? Put your number skills to the test with this problem!

a.   Work with your team to find six pairs of numbers, represented here by the variables x and y, that will make $\frac{x}{y}$ equivalent to $\frac{2}{5}$.

b.   Follow your teacher's directions to contribute your points to the class data table and graph.

c.   With your team, consider the following questions and how your answers might affect your graph. Add information to your graph as needed.

   - What happens when $x = 0$? How can you show this on the graph?

   - What happens when $x = 0.5$? How can you show this on the graph?

   - Are there any other points that have coordinates that are not whole numbers? How could you represent *all* of them?

   - What happens when $x = -2$? How can you show this on the graph?

   - Are there any other points that have coordinates that are not positive? How could you represent all of them?

Making Connections: Course 1

8-52. What can we learn from the graph? What information can the graph tell us about the pairs of numbers x and y that make $\frac{x}{y} = \frac{2}{5}$? Discuss this with your team and be prepared to contribute your ideas to a class discussion. As you talk with your team, consider the following questions.

- As the x values get larger, what happens to the y values?

- Do we see any possible points on the graph where x is positive and y is negative? Why does this **make sense**?

- How many pairs of numbers make this rule true?

8-53. Work with your team to find all of the pairs of whole numbers that can be multiplied to get 24. (Note that we say that all of these pairs of numbers satisfy the **rule** $xy = 24$.) Write these pairs of numbers in an xy- table, as shown below.

x	-4		-2	-1	1		3	4
y		-8				12		

a. On your own graph paper, graph all of your points.

b. Can you find any pairs of numbers that multiply to get 24 that are not whole numbers? Work with your team to think of a few and then add these to your table and, if they fit, to your graph.

c. What can we learn from the graph? Discuss with your team how you can see answers to the following questions in the graph. Be prepared to share your ideas with the class.

- As the x values get larger, what happens to the y values?

- Are there any points on the graph that have a positive x-value and a negative y-value? Why does this **make sense**?

- How many pairs of numbers can multiply to equal 24?

- What is special about 0? As x gets close to 0, what happens to y?

8-54. As you have seen, one method for graphing an equation with two variables, also called a **rule**, is to find pairs of values that make the equation true, graph points for these pairs of numbers, and then connect the points or extend the curve, as appropriate.

Work with your team to find pairs of values that satisfy each of the following rules. For each rule, organize the values into an x-y table.

a. $x + y = 1$ b. $xy = -1$ c. $x - y = 1$

8-55. Your teacher will assign your team one rule from problem 8-54. Work with your team to make a complete graph of your rule.

8-56.   LEARNING LOG

In your Learning Log, **explain** how you can make a
graph that allows you to plot points with negative
x- and/or y-values. Be sure to plot example points to
demonstrate your ideas. Title this entry "Graphing
Negative Coordinates" and label it with today's date.

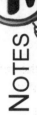

Mᴇᴛʜᴏᴅs ᴀɴᴅ Mᴇᴀɴɪɴɢs

Making Graphs of Rules

MATH NOTES

A graph of a rule (equation) represents all of the points that
make that equation true. In order to make a graph for a rule, it is often
useful to make an xy- table by finding pairs of numbers x and y that
make the rule true. Then each of the points is plotted on a graph.
Whether or not the points are connected with a line or smooth curve
depends on the rule and the context of the problem. Thus, not all
graphs are continuous, that is, you have to think about whether or not
to connect all of the points.

For example, to graph the rule $xy = 12$, you can start by
thinking of numbers that will work. For example, $x = 2$
and $y = 6$ works, because $2 \cdot 6 = 12$. This point would go
in the table, as shown at right. Another example of a
point that works is $(-1, -12)$, because $(-1)(-12) = 12$.

x	y
2	6
-1	-12

When you have a good number of points in
your table, draw a pair of xy-axes on grid
paper. Decide on a scale that will allow an
appropriate number of points to fit on the
graph. Then plot each point from the table.
To show that an infinite number of points
between the plotted ones also satisfy the rule,
connect the points with a smooth curve or
line. To show that there are infinite solutions
beyond the ones shown on the graph, draw

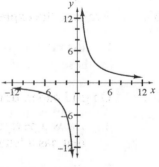

arrowheads on each end of the curve or line. A graph for the rule
$xy = 12$ is shown at right. Notice that this graph is not continuous,
since there is no point on the y-axis.

8-57.   Two angles whose measurements give a sum of 180° are called
         supplementary angles. Two angles whose measurements give a sum of 90° are
         called **complementary angles**. Use the properties of complementary, and
         supplementary angles to determine the value of each variable in the following
         figures. Do not use a protractor.

a.

b.

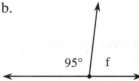

8-58.   For each of the following pairs of fractions, complete the fraction on the right so
         that the two fractions are equivalent. Using a Giant One might be helpful.

a. $\frac{30}{35} = \frac{6}{\square}$ b. $\frac{8}{40} = \frac{\square}{5}$ c. $\frac{-15}{-20} = \frac{\square}{4}$

8-59.   At right is a graph of seven coordinate points that
         satisfy the same rule.

a.   Organize the points by completing the table below.

x	–3	–2	–1	0	1	2	3
y		0.5					

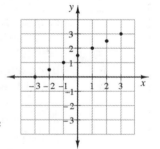

b.   Name at least two other points that satisfy the same
      rule as these.

8-60.   Evaluate the expressions below using $a = 3$, $b = -4$, $c = 5$.

a. $2a + c$ b. $12 - (a + b + c)$ c. $ab - 7$

8-61.   On grid paper, draw a rectangle with a width of 4 units and a length of 5 units.

a.   Draw a new rectangle that is an enlarged copy of your original rectangle
      that has a length of 12 units.

b.   Show how you can calculate the width of your new rectangle.

8-62.   Kate has five sandwiches to share with 3 of her friends. If each person gets the
         same amount of sandwich, how much will each person get?

8.3.1   How else can I use variables?

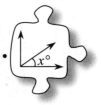

New Contexts For Variables

In the last section, you used variables and expressions to generalize a pattern. In this section, you will use variables to represent unknown amounts, as you look at some new contexts and use what you *do* know to find these unknowns.

8-63.   LUMBER LENGTHS

Jeff enjoys working with wood and solving challenging math problems. For parts (a) through (d) below, work with your team to:

- Draw a diagram to represent the situation. (A diagram for part (a) has been provided for you.)

- Use your diagram to write an equation that represents the situation.

- Find the value of x for the given situation.

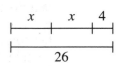

a.   Jeff cut a 26 foot piece of lumber to create four foot piece and two other pieces of equal length. How long is each of the other pieces?

b.   Jeff had a 33 foot board. He cut off 10 feet, and then wanted to cut what was left into two pieces of equal length. How long would each of the two pieces be?

c.   There are three boards of the same unknown length and a seven foot board in Jeff's shop. If the total length of all four boards is 22 feet, how long is each of the three pieces of equal length?

d.   Jeff has five boards of equal but unknown length. He takes two of them and an eight foot board, and lays them down end to end. Next to these boards, he lays down the other three boards of unknown length and one that is only two feet long. He finds that the total length of each row is the same. How long are his five unknown boards?

8-64.   AJENI'S AGES

Ajeni is trying to figure out the age of
her cousin Lane. She knows that
Nate is one year older than Lane, and
Kolby is five years older than Lane.
She also knows that the sum of the
ages of the three boys (Lane, Nate,
and Kolby) is 39. Ajeni decided to
let x represent Lane's age.

a.   Work with your team to solve
      Ajeni's problem. That is, find
      Lane's age.

b.   Ajeni noticed a connection to the lumber problems in
      problem 8-63. She decided to draw a straight line
      diagram to represent this problem. Part of her
      diagram is shown at right.

      Describe how Ajeni's diagram represents the problem. Then copy and
      complete her diagram. How can you use her diagram to find the answer?

8-65.   Alexander and Santiago were working
         with pattern blocks when they found an
         interesting relationship. They discovered
         that the 60 degree angle of the green
         triangle and four of the smaller angles of
         the beige rhombuses, laid together, create
         a straight line. A diagram of this situation
         is shown at right. Work with your team to
         find the measure of the smaller angle of
         the beige rhombus.

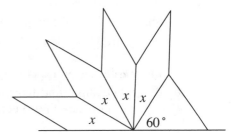

8-66. The problems below describe other situations where some angles have been put together to create larger angles. For each problem below, write an equation to represent the situation and then answer the question.

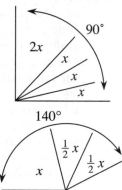

a. Three angles that all have the same measure and one angle that has a measure twice as large as the others combine to make a 90° angle, as shown in the diagram at right. What are the measures of each of the angles?

b. One angle and two other angles that are each half as large as the first combine to create an angle that measures 140°, as shown in the diagram at right. What are the measures of each of the angles?

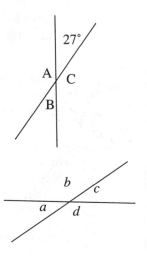

8-67. Find the measure of the unknown angles in the figure at right (that is, the angles marked A, B and C). What do you notice about the measures of these angles?

8-68. Angles that are formed by intersecting straight lines and are directly across from one another, like angles A and C in problem 8-67, are called **vertical angles**. Do these angles always have the same relationship as the one that you found in problem 8-67? Use the diagram at right and work with your team to decide if you can **explain** why this relationship would always be true.

8-69. SEAN'S SHOPPING

Sean went shopping for school supplies. He bought a pencil, a compass and a notebook and spent a total of $2.00. He noticed that the compass cost 3 times as much as the pencil and the notebook cost 4 times as much as the pencil.

a. Complete the diagram at right to represent the total cost of Sean's items.

b. How much did each item cost?

8-70.   POLKA'S DOTS

Examine the dot pattern at right.
Assume it grows by adding a new
column of two dots each time.

•   • •   • • •

•   • •   • • •

Figure 1   Figure 2   Figure 3

a.   How many dots will be in the 7th figure? What about the 50th figure? How can you tell how many will be in *any* figure?

b.   Use your ideas from part (a) to write an algebraic expression to represent the number of dots in the any figure. Use a variable, such as n, to represent the figure number.

c.   Use your expression to calculate the number of dots in the 30th figure.

d.   Which figure will have 160 dots? 101 dots? How can you show this with your expression?

METHODS AND MEANINGS

MATH NOTES

Variables

A **variable** is a letter that represents one or more numbers. In a diagram or expression, if the variable appears more that once it must represent the same number each time. As an example, look at the diagram below right that represents the number of tiles needed to surround a rectangle.

If $x = 7$, the sides are each 7 and the top and bottom are each $7 + 5 = 12$.

If $x = 11$, the sides are each 11 and the top and bottom are each $11 + 5 = 16$.

If $x = 3\frac{1}{2}$, the sides are each $3\frac{1}{2}$ and the top and bottom are each $3\frac{1}{2} + 5 = 8\frac{1}{2}$.

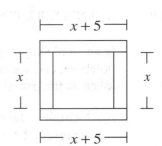

8-71.   Complete each of the webs below.

a.

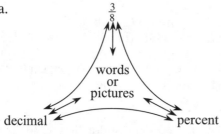

Representations of a Portion

b.

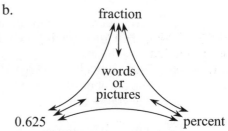

Representations of a Portion

8-72.   Write an equation that represents each diagram below and find the value of the variable.

a.

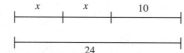

b.

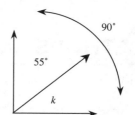

8-73   Copy and complete each of the Diamond Problems below. The pattern used in the Diamond Problems is shown at right.

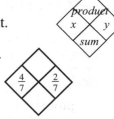

a.

b.

c.

8-74.   Arrange these numbers from greatest to least.

$$\frac{1}{3}, \ 3, \ 0.3, \ 3\frac{1}{2}, \ 0.03$$

8-75.   If $1\frac{1}{2}$ pounds of bananas cost $1.48, how much would $2\frac{1}{2}$ pounds cost? Show your work or **explain** your reasoning.

8-76.   Add or subtract the following pairs of fractions and mixed numbers.

a. $\frac{5}{6}+\frac{2}{3}$ b. $\frac{7}{8}-\frac{1}{2}$ c. $1\frac{2}{3}+1\frac{1}{4}$ d. $2\frac{1}{3}-1\frac{5}{6}$

Making Connections: Course 1

8.3.2 How can I find a missing angle?

Finding Unknown Angles in Triangles

In today's lesson, you will be challenged again to use what you *do* know to deduce information that you did *not* previously know, in order to solve problems with variables. You will do an investigation to learn a new geometric relationship for triangles.

8-77. Quealey was excited about his new talent for using variables to solve problems. He went home and grabbed his older brother Warren's math book and tried to find some problems that he could do with variables. He came across the following problem that he wanted to solve:

Solve for x in this figure:

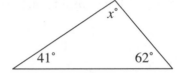

a. Using what you have learned about angles, can you find the measure of the angle? Why or why not?

b. Estimate the measure of the angle.

8-78. TANGLED TRIANGLES

Your teacher will give your team a copy of the Lesson 8.3.2 Resource Page. Cut out the three copies of the triangle.

Your task: Figure out the measure of the missing angle *without* using a protractor. As you work with your team, these question might help guide your discussion:

What do we know about angles?

Can we combine the unknown angle with any other angles
to create a new angle that we *do* know?

8-79. Be prepared to contribute what your team has discovered to a whole-class discussion. Your teacher will use a technology tool to show what each team has discovered for their triangle. Keep track of what each team has found to see if you can find a relationship that would allow you to find a missing angle in *any* triangle.

8-80.   Now, use what you have discovered about the angles in a triangle to find the answer to the problem that Quealey was trying to solve in problem 8-77. How close was your estimate?

8-81.   Use what you have learned about triangles and angles to write an equation that represents each situation. Then find each of the missing angle(s) in the triangles below.

a.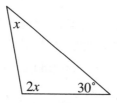

b.

8-82.   **Additional Challenge:** Use what you know about triangles and angle relationships to find the missing angle(s) in the triangles below.

a.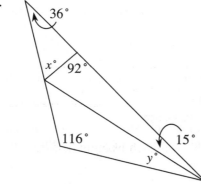

b.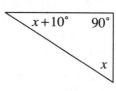

c.

d.

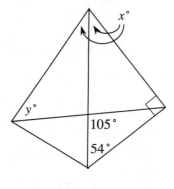

8-83.   LEARNING LOG

Today you learned about a very fundamental concept about a triangle and the sum of its angles. In your Learning Log, state this relationship in your own words and include at least one example that shows how to use this idea. Title this entry "Angles in a Triangle" and label it with today's date.

METHODS AND **M**EANINGS

MATH NOTES

Angle Relationships

It is common to identify angles using three letters. For example, $\angle ABC$ means the angle you would find by going from point A to point B to point C in the diagram at right. B is the **vertex** of the angle and BA and BC are the **rays** that define it.

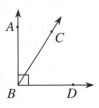

If two angles have measures that add up to 90°, they are called **complementary angles**. For example, in the diagram at right, $\angle ABC$ and $\angle CBD$ are complementary because together they form a right angle.

If two angles have measures that add up to 180°, they are called **supplementary angles**. For example, in the diagram at right, $\angle EFG$ and $\angle GFH$ are supplementary because together they form a straight angle.

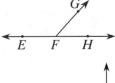

Two angles do not have to share a vertex to be complementary or supplementary. The first pair of angles at right are supplementary; the second pair of angles are complementary.

Supplementary   **Complementary**

Review & Preview

8-84.   Find the measure of the missing angle in each triangle below.

a.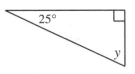

b.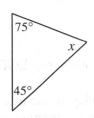

8-85.   Write an equation that represents the diagram below and find the value of *n*.

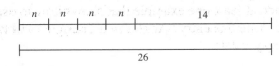

8-86. On problem 8-30 you wrote variable expressions to go with diagrams. Use what you learned to write a variable expression for the diagram shown at right.

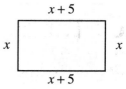

a. Write the **word** that describes the shape.

b. Write a **variable expression** that describes the perimeter of the shape.

c. If the perimeter is 26 inches, what is the value of x?

8-87. Clara is taking advantage of a sale at Shari's Shoes and wants to figure out how much she will save on a pair of boots that cost $112. The sale is for 15% off. Clara's percent ruler is shown at right. Copy the ruler onto your paper and help her figure out what 15% of $112 is.

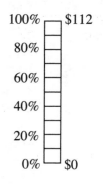

8-88. Convert each of the following portions to the representations described. Show your work so that a team member could understand your process.

a. Write $\frac{3}{5}$ as a decimal and a percent.

b. Write 0.7 as a fraction and a percent.

c. Write 16% as a fraction and a decimal.

d. Write 2.45 as a percent and a fraction.

8-89. For each of the diagrams below, identify each set of angles as complementary, supplementary, vertical, or none. **Explain** how you know.

a.

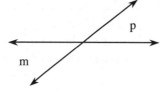

b.

c.

d.

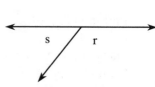

e.

f.

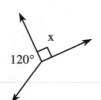

Making Connections: Course 1

$8.4.1$ How can I divide?

....

Dividing by Fractions

$1\frac{1}{2} \div 4\frac{1}{2}$

Throughout this course, you have learned about working with portions in many representations. You have learned to operate with and on fractions, multiplying, adding, and subtracting. In this section, you will **connect** many ideas you have worked with as you learn to *divide* fractions. As you work on the problems in this lesson, ask your teammates the following questions to spark useful discussion:

> How can we represent this with a diagram?

> Is there **another way to see** it?

8-90. Phillip is preparing to serve dessert to a large group of his family and friends. When he called to order three pies from the local bakery, he was told that each pie would be cut into pieces that are each $\frac{1}{8}$ of a pie.

   a. How many pieces of pie will he have in all? Be prepared to **explain** your answer to the class.

   b. Work with your team to represent this problem and its answer using a mathematical sentence.

8-91. Phillip also plans to order five large brownies. He has decided to cut them into serving portions that are each $\frac{2}{3}$ of a brownie. How many portions will he have? Work with your team to draw a diagram to help **make sense** of this problem. Then write the problem and its answer as a mathematical sentence.

8-92. Phillip decides to increase his order to seven brownies. He still plans to divide the brownies into portions that are each $\frac{2}{3}$ of a brownie. To figure out how many portions he will have to serve, he calculated $7 \div \frac{2}{3} = 10\frac{1}{2}$. Work with your team to **explain** to Phillip what his answer means. What does the number $10\frac{1}{2}$ tell him about his brownies?

8-93.   Sala is building a dollhouse for her cousin. She needs boards that are each $\frac{3}{4}$ of a foot long. She called the store and found that the lumber she needs is sold only in lengths of eight feet. How many of her $\frac{3}{4}$-foot boards can she cut from each eight foot piece? How much lumber will be left over?

METHODS AND **M**EANINGS

Triangle Angle Sum Theorem

MATH NOTES

The **Triangle Angle Sum Theorem** states that the measures of the angles in a triangle add up to 180°. For example, in $\triangle ABC$ at right:

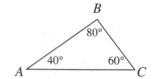

$$m\angle A + m\angle B + m\angle C = 180°$$

The Triangle Angle Sum Theorem can be verified by using a tiling of the given triangle (shaded at right). Because the tiling produces parallel lines, the alternate interior angles must be congruent. As seen in the diagram at right, the three angles of a triangle form a straight angle. Therefore, the sum of the angles of a triangle must be 180°.

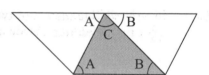

8-94.   Calculate each of the following quotients.

   a. $4 \div \frac{1}{3}$ b. $6 \div \frac{2}{3}$

8-95.   If four boxes of chocolate have a combined weight of 2.6 pounds, how many
         pounds would 11 boxes of chocolate weigh? Show how you know.

8-96.   Find the measure of the missing angle in each triangle below.

   a.   b.

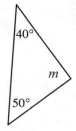   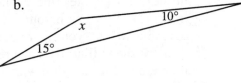

8-97.   Jesse has five meters of twine and he needs to cut it into lengths that are each
         $\frac{1}{4}$ of a meter long. How many lengths will he have?

8-98.   Evaluate the expressions below using $x = -2$, $y = -5$, and $z = 3$.

   a. xyz b. $3(x + y)$ c. $\frac{z+2}{y} + 1$

8-99.   Copy and complete the table at right with values of x and y that
         work for the rule $xy = 40$.

x	y
8	
10	
−2	
	1
$\frac{1}{2}$	
	−1
400	

8.4.2 How can I divide?

Division of Fractions

In the previous lesson you learned how to divide whole numbers by fractions less than one. In this lesson, you will extend your understanding to include division of fractions by other fractions.

8-100. Judy is writing a piece of music. She has decided to replace a $\frac{3}{4}$ note (this takes up $\frac{3}{4}$ of a measure, or a small section of the music) with $\frac{1}{8}$ notes (these take up $\frac{1}{8}$ of a measure). Work with your team to use diagrams to help you figure out how many $\frac{1}{8}$ notes she will need. Then represent the problem and its solution with a mathematical sentence. Be prepared to **describe** your strategies to the class.

8-101. DIVISION CHALLENGE

Work with your team to draw diagrams to help you calculate each of the following quotients. Keep track of the strategies that are most useful for you and be ready to **explain** them to the class.

a. $\frac{3}{4} \div \frac{3}{8}$

b. $\frac{3}{4} \div \frac{1}{2}$

8-102. Why is each answer in problem 8-101 greater than one? Work with your team to write and solve a fraction division problem that has an answer less than one. Be ready to share your problem with the class.

8-103. The diagram below can be used to calculate $\frac{3}{4} \div \frac{3}{8}$. (This sort of a diagram is often referred to as a linear model.)

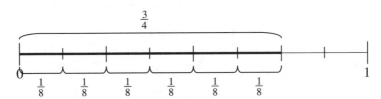

a. Work with your team to **make sense** of this model. Be prepared to **explain** how this model works and how you can see the answer in this model.

b. Use a linear model to show the solution for $\frac{3}{4} \div \frac{1}{2}$.

8-104. Work with your team to find a strategy for dividing fractions without drawing a diagram. Be prepared to **explain** your strategy to the class.

MᴇᴛʜODS AND Mᴇᴀɴɪɴɢs

Angle Pair Relationships

MATH NOTES

Adjacent angles are angles that have a common vertex. So angles $\angle c$ and $\angle d$ in the diagram at right are adjacent angles, as are $\angle c$ and $\angle f$.

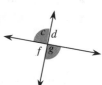

Vertical angles are the two opposite (that is, non-adjacent) angles formed by two intersecting lines, such as angles $\angle c$ and $\angle g$ in the diagram at right. $\angle c$ by itself is not a vertical angle, nor is $\angle g$, although $\angle c$ and $\angle g$ together are a pair of vertical angles. Vertical angles always have equal measure.

8-105.   Divide each of the following pairs of fractions.

    a. $\frac{2}{3} \div \frac{1}{12}$ b. $\frac{5}{6} \div \frac{5}{12}$ c. $\frac{5}{6} \div \frac{3}{12}$

8-106.   Jamie has 9 gallons of paint that she needs to pour into containers that hold
          $\frac{3}{4}$ of a gallon. How many containers will she need?

8-107.   Find the value of the variable that makes each equation true.

    a. $x + 9 = 20$ b. $-3x = -15$

8-108.   Use the correct order of operations to simplify the following expressions.

    a. $(6-8)(9-10)-(4+2)(6+3)$ b. $\frac{-84}{32-12(-5)}$

    c. $-4(7)+2(-3\frac{1}{8})$ d. $56-(-4)+-6(4\frac{2}{3})$

8-109.   Let x represent the cost of a drink, y represent the cost of a sandwich, and z
          represent the cost of potatoes at *Quick and Cheap Drive Through*. Manaya
          placed an order at the drive through, and the cost of her order is represented by
          the diagram below.

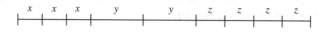

    a.   According to the diagram, how many of each item did Manaya order?

    b.   Use Manaya's diagram to write a variable expression that represents the
         cost of the order she placed.

    c.   If drinks cost $0.79, sandwiches cost $3.29 and potatoes cost $0.99, find the
         value of the expression you wrote in part (b). In other words, find the total
         cost of her order.

8.4.3 How can I divide?

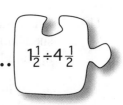

Division with Mixed Numbers and Decimals

In this lesson, you will continue your work with dividing fractions to include strategies for dividing mixed numbers and decimals.

8-110. Students in Ms. Sullivan's class were discussing their strategies for dividing fractions. They each made claims about general strategies that they think will work for dividing fractions. Work with your team to decide whether each of the algorithms proposed below will work in all cases. Be prepared to **explain** your thinking to the class.

Dria's method: *"When I divide $\frac{2}{3} \div \frac{1}{6}$, I get 4. I think this is because $\frac{2}{3}$ is the same as $\frac{4}{6}$ and $\frac{4}{6} \div \frac{1}{6}$ is the same as $4 \div 1$, which equals 4. So I think that I can always make both fraction have a common denominator and then just divide the numerators to get my answer."*

Kelvyon's method: *"When I divide $\frac{4}{9} \div \frac{1}{3}$, I get $\frac{4}{3}$. I think this is because $4 \cdot 1 = 4$ and $9 \div 3 = 3$. So I think that I can always multiply the numerators and divide the denominators to get my answer."*

Anthony's method: *"When I divide $\frac{4}{7} \div \frac{2}{3}$, I get $\frac{6}{7}$. I think this is because $\frac{4}{7} \cdot 3 = \frac{12}{7}$, and $\frac{12}{7} \div 2 = \frac{6}{7}$. So I think that I can always multiply the first fraction by the denominator of the second fraction, and then divide that answer by the numerator of the second fraction."*

8-111. William used $2\frac{1}{2}$ cups of ricotta cheese in his famous lasagna recipe. He cut the lasagna into 12 servings. How much cheese is there in each portion?

8-112. Mr. Royer ordered too much pizza for the tennis team's spring party. After the party, there were $5\frac{1}{2}$ pizzas left. If the pizzas are cut into pieces that are $\frac{1}{12}$ of a pizza, how many pieces are left?

8-113. Gloria is planning a $17\frac{1}{2}$-mile hike. If she stops to rest every $1\frac{3}{4}$ miles, how many rest stops will she make?

8-114. Anna wants to find the **quotient** (answer to a division problem) $0.6 \div 0.25$, but she is not sure how to divide decimals. Her sister, Elsha, suggests she rewrite the numbers as fractions since they know how to divide fractions.

   a. With your team, rewrite $0.6 \div 0.25$ using fractions and use what you know about dividing fractions to find an answer that is *one* fraction.

   b. *"Hmm,"* said Anna, *"Since the original problem was written with decimals, I should probably write my answer as a decimal."* Convert the answer from part (a) to a decimal.

   c. Find the quotient $1.29 \div 0.06$.

8-115. Elsha wants to divide $0.07 \div 0.4$ and thinks she sees a shortcut. *"Can I just divide $7 \div 4$?"* she wonders.

   a. What do you think? Will Elsha's shortcut work? Determine why or why not, and be prepared to share your ideas with the class.

   b. Determine the answer to $0.07 \div 0.4$, and show how you found your answer.

8-116. Show your work as you complete each of the following problems.

   a. $8\frac{1}{10} \div 1\frac{1}{2}$ b. $\frac{5}{2} \div \frac{3}{3}$ c. $\frac{3}{5} \cdot 1\frac{4}{7}$ d. $\frac{5}{5} \div \frac{2}{3}$

   e. $\frac{1}{2} \div \frac{2}{3}$ f. $\frac{0}{3} \div \frac{9}{7}$ g. $\frac{8}{7} + \frac{11}{11}$ h. $\frac{0}{5} \cdot \frac{2}{9}$

8-117. Work with your team to write two word problems *on separate paper*, one that involves division of fractions or mixed numbers and one that involves multiplication of fractions or mixed numbers. Then solve the problems on your own paper. Be prepared to share your problems so that other students can solve them.

METHODS AND MEANINGS

Dividing Fractions

Method 1: Dividing Fractions using Multiplication

To divide any number by a fraction using multiplication, multiply the first number by the denominator of the second fraction and then divide the result by the numerator of the second fraction. For example, to divide $\frac{2}{5} \div \frac{3}{10}$, start by multiplying $\frac{2}{5}$ by 10 and then divide by 3, as shown below.

$$\frac{2}{5} \div \frac{3}{10} = \frac{2}{5} \cdot 10 \div 3$$
$$= 4 \div 3$$
$$= \frac{4}{3}$$
$$= 1\frac{1}{3}$$

Method 2: Dividing Fractions using Common Denominators

To divide a number by a fraction using common denominators, express both numbers as fractions with the same denominator. Then divide the first numerator by the second. For example,

$$\frac{2}{5} \div \frac{3}{10} = \frac{4}{10} \div \frac{3}{10}$$
$$= \frac{4}{3}$$
$$= 1\frac{1}{3}$$

Review & Preview

8-118.   The Giant One lets you change a decimal division problem into a whole number division problem. Copy the example below and complete the other problems in the same manner.

	Decimal Division Problem	Multiply by Giant 1	Whole Number Division Problem	Answer
Example	$\frac{2.5}{0.25}$	$\frac{2.5}{0.25} \cdot \frac{100}{100} = \frac{250}{25}$	$25\overline{)250}$	10
	$\frac{1.4}{0.7}$	$\frac{1.4}{0.7} \cdot \frac{10}{10} =$		
	$\frac{520}{0.013}$	$\frac{520}{0.013} \cdot \frac{1000}{1000} =$		
	$8.2 \div 0.4$	$\frac{8.2}{0.4} \cdot \frac{?}{?} =$		
	$0.02 \div 0.005$			
	$10.05 \div 0.25$			

8-119.   Mandy has a bag of blueberries, raspberries, and blackberries. Mandy says that the probability of randomly selecting a raspberry is $\frac{18}{17}$, but her brother, Tony, says that does not **make sense**. **Explain** how Tony knows that this probability does not **make sense**, without even knowing how many of each berry are in the bag.

8-120.   Find the value of the variable that makes each equation true.

    a. $x + 10 = 2$ b. $2x + 8 = 18$

8-121.   **Adjacent angles** are angles that share a common side and vertex but no common interior points. Examine the measured pairs of angles below and choose the pair that is adjacent. **Explain** why your choice is correct. Also identify any measured angle pairs as complementary, supplementary, or vertical.

    a.

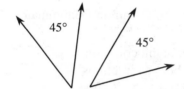

    b.

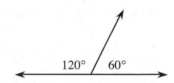

    c.

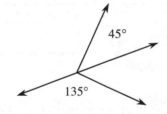

    d.

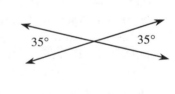

8-122.   If a train travels at 45 miles every hour, how far will it have traveled after each of the following amounts of time? Show how you found your answer.

    a.   2 hours?   b.   5 hours?   c. $7\frac{1}{2}$ hours?

8-123.   Find the value of each of the following expressions.

    a. $\frac{11}{12} + \frac{4}{9}$ b. $4\frac{3}{5} - 1\frac{13}{15}$ c. $\frac{9}{10} \cdot 2\frac{1}{3}$ d. $12 \div \frac{7}{8}$

Chapter 8 Closure   What have I learned?

Reflection and Synthesis

The activities below offer you a chance to reflect on what you have learned during this chapter. As you work, look for concepts that you feel very comfortable with, ideas that you would like to learn more about, and topics you need more help with. Look for **connections** between ideas as well as **connections** with material you learned previously.

①   SUMMARIZING MY UNDERSTANDING

This section gives you an opportunity to show your understanding of how variables can be used, one of the main ideas of this chapter.

Team Poster

You have been learning how to use variables and write variable expressions in different situations – both to represent a missing piece of information and to represent a general pattern or rule. You also learned strategies for finding the value of the variable in a specific situation as well as how to use the value given to you to evaluate an expression. This section gives you an opportunity to demonstrate what you know so far about these concepts. Today you and your team will create a poster that illustrates the skills and knowledge that you have developed in this area.

```
 _____
|                                   |
|     |-----------------------|     |
|     |   Title               |     |
| Situations                  |     |
|     |-----------|-----------|     |
|     |           |           |     |
|     |-----------|-----------|     |
|     |           |           |     |
|     |-----------|-----------|     |
| Problem Statement and Solution     |
|     |-----------------------|     |
|     |                       |     |
|     |-----------------------|     |
|_____|
```

Brainstorm Situations: Follow your teacher's instructions to brainstorm a list of different situations where a variable could be used to answer a question.

Situation Descriptions: Work with your team to think of four different situations for which a variable could be used. Then each person should write a description of one of the situations and suggest a variable to use for the situation. Be sure to provide enough information so that someone unfamiliar with the situation would understand what you mean.

Write a Problem: Follow your teacher's instructions to select one situation randomly. Then work with your team to use that situation to write a problem. Remember that you will need to provide all of the necessary information and details for someone else to be able to solve the problem. Show your problem to your teacher before the next step.

Activity continues on next page →

①   *Activity continued from previous page.*

Solve Your Problem: Now your team should find the answer to your problem. This should include writing a variable expression and then showing how to get the answer. Be sure to include your reasoning for your process and enough of your steps that anyone looking at it will know what you did.

Team Poster: Follow the model above to label and construct the sections of your poster from the pieces that your team has created. Decide together on a title for your poster.

②   ASSESSING MY UNDERSTANDING

Working the problems in this section will help you to evaluate which types of problems you feel comfortable with and which you need more help with.

Solve each problem as completely as you can. The table at the end of this closure section provides answers to these problems. It also tells you where you can find additional help and practice on problems like these.

CL 8-124. Draw a number line and place a point for each of the following portions on it.

a. $\frac{4}{5}$ b. 0.003   c. 30%   d. $\frac{7}{6}$

e. 0.75   f. $\frac{3}{7}$ g. $\frac{1}{3}$ h. $\frac{112}{112}$

CL 8-125. Evaluate the following algebraic expressions.

a. Find the value of $7m + 9$ for $m = 2$.

b. Find the value of $a \cdot b$ for $a = 10$ and $b = 4$.

CL 8-126. Without a calculator, simplify each of the following expressions:

a. $20 \div 2 + (-4)(-6)$ b. $5\frac{1}{2} \cdot 1\frac{1}{3}$

c. $0.4(0.05)$ d. $\frac{4}{3} \div \frac{5}{8}$

CL 8-127. Find five pairs of numbers that work for the rule $xy = 30$ and write your numbers in the form (x, y). Be sure to include negative numbers and non-integers (fractions and decimals) in your list.

418

CL 8-128. Find the missing angles in the diagrams below.

a.

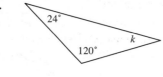

b.

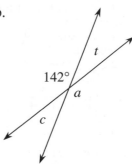

CL 8-129. Write an equation that represents each diagram and find the value of x.

a.

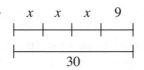

b.

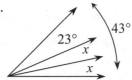

CL 8-130. Copy the dot pattern below and draw Figures 0, 4, and 7. **Describe** how the pattern is growing.

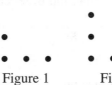

Figure 1   Figure 2   Figure 3

CL 8-131. Find the volume of the prism shown at right if the area of the base is 25 square centimeters.

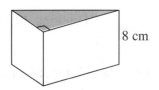

8 cm

CL 8-132. Find three fractions that are equivalent to each of the following fractions.

a. $\frac{2}{9}$

b. $\frac{50}{80}$

CL 8-133. Marcello found a guacamole recipe that calls for $\frac{1}{4}$ cup of cilantro, but he only needs three-fourths as much guacamole as the recipe would make. How much cilantro should Marcello use? Show or **explain** how you got your answer.

CL 8-134. For each of the problems above, do the following:

- Draw a bar or number line that represents 0 to 10.

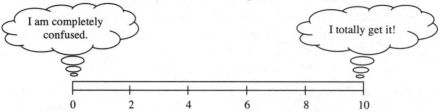

- Color or shade in a portion of the bar that represents your level of understanding and comfort with completing that problem on your own.

If any of your bars are less than a 5, choose *one* of those problems and do one of the following tasks:

- Write two questions that you would like to ask about that problem.

- Brainstorm two things that you DO know about that type of problem.

If all of your bars are at 5 or above, choose one problem and do one of these tasks:

- Write two questions you might ask or hints you might give to a student that was stuck on the problem.

- Make a new problem that is similar and more challenging than that problem and solve it.

③ SUPPORTING MY UNDERSTANDING

You have several tools and references available to help support your learning – your teacher, your study team, your math book, and your Toolkit to name only a few. At the end of each chapter you will have an opportunity to review your Toolkit for completeness as well as to revise or update your Toolkit to better reflect your current understanding of big ideas.

The main elements of your Toolkit should be your Learning Log, Math Notes and the vocabulary used in this chapter. Math words that are new to this chapter appear in bold in the text. Refer to the lists provided below and follow your teacher's instructions to revise your Toolkit, which will help make it a useful reference for you as you complete this chapter and prepare to begin the next one.

Learning Log Entries
- Lesson 8.2.4 – Graphing Negative Coordinates
- Lesson 8.3.2 – Angles in a Triangle

Math Notes
- Lesson 8.2.2 – Describing Growth Patterns
- Lesson 8.2.3 – Using a Variable to Generalize
- Lesson 8.2.4 – Making Graphs of Rules
- Lesson 8.3.1 – Variables
- Lesson 8.3.2 – Angle Relationships
- Lesson 8.4.1 – Triangle Angle Sum Theorem
- Lesson 8.4.2 – Angle Pair Relationships
- Lesson 8.4.3 – Dividing Fractions

Mathematical Vocabulary
The following is a list of vocabulary found in this chapter. Some of the words have been seen in the previous chapter. The words in bold are the words new to this chapter. Make sure that you are familiar with the terms below and know what they mean. For the words you do not know, refer to the glossary or index. You might also add these words to your Toolkit so that you can reference them in the future.

adjacent angles	**expression**	**complementary angles**
evaluate	**reciprocal**	**rule**
supplementary angles	**variable**	**vertical angles**

Process Words

analyze	arrange	combine
convert	generalize	graph
simplify	solve	substitute

Answers and Support for Closure Activity #2
Assessing My Understanding

Problem	Solution	Need Help?	More Practice
CL 8-124.	30% 0.003 $\frac{1}{3}$ $\frac{3}{7}$ 0.75 $\frac{4}{5}$ $\frac{112}{112}$ $\frac{7}{6}$	Lessons 6.2.4, 6.3.1, and 6.3.2 Math Notes box in Lesson 6.3.2 Learning Log (problems 6-131 and 7-64)	Problems 8-33, 8-74, and 8-88
CL 8-125.	a. $7(2)+9 = 14+9 = 23$ b. $10 \cdot 4 = 40$	Lesson 8.2.3 Math Notes boxes in Lessons 8.2.3 and 8.3.1	Problems 8-41, 8-46, 8-60, 8-98, and 8-109
CL 8-126.	a. 34 b. $\frac{22}{3}$ or $7\frac{1}{3}$ c. 0.02 d. $\frac{32}{15}$ or $2\frac{2}{15}$	Lesson 7.2.2, 7.2.4, 7.2.5, and 7.3.1 Math Notes box in Lesson 7.3.1 Learning Log (problem 7-87)	Problems 8-91, 8-50, 8-116, and 8-123
CL 8-127.	Some possible (x, y) pairs are shown in the table at right. There are many others. <table><tr><td>x</td><td>y</td></tr><tr><td>-6</td><td>-5</td></tr><tr><td>$-\frac{1}{2}$</td><td>-60</td></tr><tr><td>1</td><td>30</td></tr><tr><td>1.5</td><td>20</td></tr><tr><td>$\frac{12}{5}$</td><td>$\frac{25}{5}$</td></tr></table>	Lessons 8.2.3 and 8.2.4 Math Notes box in Lessons 8.2.3 and 8.2.4 Learning Log (problem 8-56)	Problems 8-51, 8-53, 8-54, and 8-99
CL 8-128.	a. $k = 36°$ b. $a = 142°, t = 38°, c = 38°$	Lessons 8.2.3 and 8.3.1 Math Notes box in Lesson 8.3.1 Learning Log (problem 8-83)	Problems 8-65, 8-77, 8-81, 8-82, and 8-84

Problem	Solution	Need Help?	More Practice
CL 8-129.	a. $x + x + x + 9 = 30$ $x = 7$ b. $x + x + 23° = 43°$ $x = 10°$	Lessons 8.2.3, 8.3.1, and 8.3.2 Math Notes boxes in Lessons 8.2.3 and 8.3.1	Problems 8-63, 8-64, 8-69, and 8-66
CL 8-130.	 Figure 0 Figure 4 Figure 7	Lesson 8.1.1 Math Notes box in Lesson 8.2.2	Problems 8-1, 8-2, 8-3, 8-8, and 8-14
CL 8-131.	$V = 200$ cubic cm	Lesson 7.1.2 Math Notes box in Lesson 7.2.1 Learning Log (problem 7-19)	Problems 7-17, 7-20, and 7-80
CL 8-132.	Answers vary; sample answers: a. $\frac{4}{18}, \frac{6}{27}, \frac{20}{90}$ b. $\frac{5}{8}, \frac{10}{16}, \frac{500}{800}$	Lessons 6.3.1 and 6.3.2 Math Notes box in Lesson 6.3.2 Learning Log (problems 6-121 and 6-131)	Problems 6-119, 6-120, and 6-130
CL 8-133.	$\frac{3}{16}$ cups; Sample explanation: Marcello needs to make $\frac{3}{4}$ of a whole recipe, so he only needs $\frac{3}{4}$ of the $\frac{1}{4}$ cups needed to make a whole recipe, $\frac{3}{4} \cdot \frac{1}{4} = \frac{3}{16}$.	Lessons 6.2.2 and 6.2.3 Math Notes box in Lesson 6.2.4 Learning Log (problem 6-64)	Problems 8-16, 8-87, and 8-106

Percents, Proportions, and Geometry

CHAPTER 9   Percents, Proportions, and Geometry

In Section 9.1, you will think about percents again. However, this time you will learn strategies for calculating percents in useful applications, such as calculating discounts, tips and interest earned.

In Section 9.2, you will study a special kind of a relationship, known as a proportional relationship. You will learn to identify which relationships are proportional and which are not by looking at them in tables and on graphs.

In Section 9.3, you will extend your understanding of geometry to include volume of shapes in three dimensions.

In this chapter, you will learn how to:

➢ Calculate percentages using mental math strategies.

➢ Recognize proportional relationships in tables and graphs.

➢ Use your understanding of proportions to make predictions and solve problems.

➢ Calculate volume of some three dimensional shapes.

Guiding Questions

Think about these questions throughout this chapter:

What is the relationship?

How can I see it in a table?

How can I see it on a graph?

What can I measure?

Does it make sense?

Chapter Outline

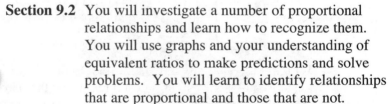
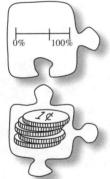

Section 9.1 You will develop strategies for calculating percentages to solve problems involving tips, interest, sale prices, and discounts.

Section 9.2 You will investigate a number of proportional relationships and learn how to recognize them. You will use graphs and your understanding of equivalent ratios to make predictions and solve problems. You will learn to identify relationships that are proportional and those that are not.

Section 9.3 You will investigate triangles to find a relationship between base, height, and area and you will learn to calculate area of circles. You will then apply these ideas to shapes in three dimensions, calculating volumes of cylinders and triangle-based prisms.

9.1.1 Which is sweeter?

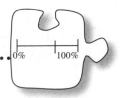

Multiplicative Growth and Percents

Have you ever mixed a powdered drink or soup and found it to be too watery or too strong? In this lesson, you will use math to **compare** the concentration (or strength) of two mixtures. As you work with your team, ask the following questions:

How do these mixtures **compare**?

How can we represent it?

How can we convince someone this is true?

9-1. WHICH IS SWEETER?

Kay and Bill love hummingbirds. Every spring, they hang feeders around their gardens full of the mixture of water and corn syrup the birds enjoy eating. Today they are **comparing** the sweetness of their recipes, shown at right.

Kay's Recipe
2 quarts water
3 cups corn syrup

Bill thinks his is sweeter. *"Mine has 5 cups of corn syrup and yours only has 3!"*

Bill's Recipe
2 gallons water
5 cups corn syrup

Kay thinks hers is sweeter. *"But mine has a higher percentage of corn syrup,"* she argues.

a. Work with your team to **make sense** of each person's argument.

b. Help Kay and Bill calculate the percentage of corn syrup in each person's recipe. They have found the conversion information below to help.

1 gallon = 4 quarts = 16 cups

c. Which information is most important to decide which food is sweeter: the amount of corn syrup in each recipe, or the percentage of corn syrup? Which recipe is sweeter? Discuss this with your team and be prepared to **explain** your ideas to the class.

9-2. Kay read that hummingbirds prefer food that is approximately 20% corn syrup. If she wants to make 8 quarts of this hummingbird food, how much corn syrup should she use? Work with your team to find **at least two ways** to solve this problem and be prepared to share your ideas with the class.

9-3. What if Bill wanted to make $7\frac{1}{2}$ gallons of a mixture that was 15% corn syrup? How could you figure out how much corn syrup he needs? Work with your team to find as many strategies as you can.

9-4. Jenna was **comparing** how much she grew in the last year with how much her baby sister grew in the same time period. Jenna's sister is 2 years old now and measures 33 inches, up 6 inches from her 1-year height. Jenna is 12 years old and measures 56 inches, up 8 inches from her height 1 year ago.

Jenna told her mother, *"Ha! I grew more than my sister."*

Her mother replied, *"Really? But I think that your sister grew by a larger percent of her height a year ago. How can you say you grew more?"*

Discuss this with your team. How can Jenna say that she grew more and her mother say that her sister grew more? Is either of them incorrect? Be ready to **explain** your ideas to the class.

9-5. Examine the snack mix recipes described below.

a. Calculate the portion of each mix below that is chocolate, expressing your answer as a percent. Which recipe has the greatest concentration of chocolate?

b. Calculate the portion of each mix that is peanuts, again expressing your answer as a percent. Which recipe has the greatest concentration of peanuts?

Recipe A:
3 cups Choc. Chips
2 cups Peanuts
2 cups Raisins
2 cups Cashews
1 cup Coconut

Recipe B:
5 cups Choc. Chips
7 cups Peanuts
4 cups Raisins
2 cups Cashews
1 cup Coconut
1 cup Almonds

Recipe C:
6 cups Choc. Chips
7 cups Peanuts
5 cups Raisins
2 cups Cashews
2 cups Coconut
3 cups Almonds

9-6.　　Alan runs in a race that is 5 miles long. Copy the number line below and use it to help determine how many miles he has completed after 72% of the race.

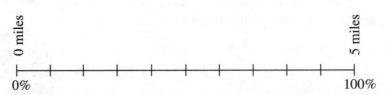

9-7.　　Simplify each of the following expressions.

　　a.　$\frac{3}{5} \div \frac{9}{7}$　　　　b.　$6 \div \frac{7}{3}$　　　　c.　$1.2 \div 0.03$　　　　d.　$5\frac{1}{2} \div 1\frac{2}{3}$

9-8.　　Malik has been thinking about division and needs to compute $5 \div \frac{3}{4}$. He knows that $2 \div 7$ is the same as $\frac{2}{7}$.

　　Malik:　　*"Since that's true, then I could just say $5 \div \frac{3}{4} = \frac{5}{\frac{3}{4}}$*

　　Cheryl:　　*"That's ugly, Malik. That's a super fraction."*

　　Malik:　　*"Yeah, but then I can use a Giant One!"*

　　Then Malik writes $\frac{5}{\frac{3}{4}} \cdot \boxed{\frac{4}{4}}$

　　a.　Complete Malik's problem by multiplying and then simplifying.

　　b.　Use Malik's method to find $3 \div \frac{2}{3}$.

9-9.　　Find the value of the variable that makes each equation true.

　　a.　$3x + 2 = 20$　　　　　　　　b.　$2x - 1 = 23$

9.1.2 How can I calculate the portion?

Composition and Decomposition of Percents

Can you imagine swimming, biking, and running for a total of 140 miles without stopping? What about directing a team of dogs as they pull a sled all the way across the state of Alaska? Athletes accomplish these exact feats each year in the Ironman Triathlon and the Iditarod dog sled race. In this lesson, you will work with your team to use your knowledge of percents to analyze portions of these amazing races.

9-10. Grant is training for the Ironman Triathlon, a 140-mile race that starts with a swim, followed by a biking portion, and ends with a run. The swimming portion is approximately 1.5% of the race. The biking portion covers about 80% of the race. The running portion covers about 18.5% of the race.

Your task: Work with your team to help Grant determine the approximate length of each of the segments of the race. Make sure to show your work.

Discussion Points

What tool will help us find the parts?

What is the whole?

How can we figure out the distance of 10% of the race? 1%?

9-11. Danielle and Nicole were working on problem 9-10, when Danielle had an idea. *"I know!"* she said. *"If we can figure out how long 10% and 1% of the race are, we can use that information to figure out each section."*

a. Discuss this idea with your team. What does Danielle mean?

b. Determine the distances in 10%, 1%, and 0.5% of the race.

c. Use this information to find the distance of each segment of the Ironman Triathlon. Do you get the same answers you got before?

Making Connections: Course 1

9-12.   When Ruby learned about the Ironman Triathlon she decided to create her own race in a similar style.

The skateboard portion of her race would be 0.25 miles. The tricycle segment would be 0.4 miles. Then there would be a 1-mile run.

a.   If the skateboard section is exactly 10% of the race, how long is the race?

b.   If the tricycle section is still 0.4 miles, what percent of the race is it?

c.   What percent of the race is the running portion?

d.   Work with your team to draw a percent ruler to represent the entire race and place each of the events on the ruler. Do your results **make sense**?

e.   *"Oh! Wait!"* said Ruby. *"I almost forgot the scooter portion of the race."* If the scooter portion is the last portion of the race, how long does it have to be?

9-13.   The Iditarod dog sled race is run each year from Anchorage to Nome, Alaska. At every rest stop throughout the race, a veterinarian checks each team of dogs.

Draw a percent ruler on your paper like the one below and use the information on the map to help you find the missing information so you can complete the table below for one team's rest stops.

0 miles

|————————————————————————————————————|
0%   100 %

Section	Distance	Percent
A	176	
B	231	
C	220	20%
D	308	
E		15%
Total		

9-14. In a 412 mile bicycle race, bicyclists complete 20% on the first day.

a. How far do they ride on this day? Show how you get your answer.

b. If they ride 21% of the race on the second day, how many miles do they ride on this day?

c. After completing the first two days as described in parts (a) and (b), what percentage of the race do they have left to ride?

d. How many miles do they have left to ride?

9-15. Ahmal was thinking about Malik's idea of using a Giant One to help divide, and realized it could be developed further. He used the problem $2\frac{1}{2} \div \frac{3}{4}$ to demonstrate his idea.

Ahmal said, *"I agree that* $2\frac{1}{2} \div \frac{3}{4} = \dfrac{2\frac{1}{2}}{\frac{3}{4}} = \dfrac{\frac{5}{2}}{\frac{3}{4}}$. *But let's not just use a regular Giant One like you did, let's use a Super Giant One!*

Then Ahmal writes: $\dfrac{\frac{5}{2}}{\frac{3}{4}} \cdot \dfrac{\frac{4}{3}}{\frac{4}{3}}$

a. Complete Ahmal's problem by multiplying and then simplifying.

b. Cheryl multiplied and got $\dfrac{\frac{20}{6}}{\frac{12}{12}}$. Then she was stuck. *"What should I do about the* $\frac{12}{12}$ *?"* she asked. **Explain** how she can finish the problem.

c. Show how to write $\frac{4}{5} \div \frac{1}{2}$ Ahmal's way; then solve it using a Super Giant One.

)

Making Connections: Course 1

9-16.   Calculate each of the following quotients.

   a. $\frac{2}{3} \div \frac{2}{5}$

   b. $\frac{5}{6} \div \frac{1}{12}$

   c. $3\frac{1}{8} \div 2\frac{1}{2}$

9-17.   Write an algebraic expression to represent the length of each segment shown below.

   a. |—— n ——|—— n ——|—— n ——|—— 15 ——|

   b. |———— 17 ————|—— x ——|—— x ——|—10—|

   c. |-$\frac{5}{5}$-$\frac{5}{5}$-$\frac{5}{5}$-|—— $2x$ ——|

9-18.   Simplify each of the following expressions without a calculator, and then use a calculator to check your answers.

   a. $0.045 + 1.2 + 62.003$

   b. $56.7 - 0.23$

   c. $7.8 \cdot 0.03$

   d. $6.3 - 7.5$

9.1.3 What is the portion?

Percent Discounts

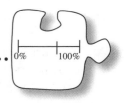

In Chapter 4 you used percent rulers to find various portions of a whole. In this lesson you will investigate this and other strategies for finding percents of a whole.

9-19. SHOPPING SHIRLEY

Shirley won a shopping spree from Dacy's Department store. She can spend up to $150 on any items in the store. During Dacy's Deal Days the store marks down their prices and pays for all sales tax! Shirley would like to buy each of the items shown in the table below. For each item, she knows the original price and the marked discount.

Item	Price	Discount	Sale Price
Scarf	$37	20%	
Dress shoes	$56	15%	
Necklace	$30	5%	
Skirt	$36	25%	
Sweater	$45	12%	
Shirt	$21	$\frac{1}{3}$ off	

Your task: Work with your team to figure out whether Shirley can afford to buy everything she wants. If not, recommend to her what she should buy to get the most out of her shopping spree.

Discussion Points

How can we find this percent?

What does this amount represent?

How much will she have to spend?

9-20.   Shirley was trying to calculate the sale price of the scarf that she wants after its original price of $37 is marked down 20%. She got out her notepad and sketched the picture below to help her **visualize** the problem.

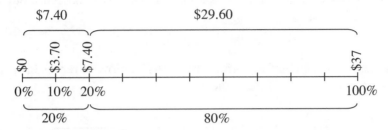

Work with your team to interpret her diagram and **explain** what $3.70, $7.40, and $29.60 mean in relationship to the cost of the scarf. Then enter the sale price of her scarf into the table from problem 9-19.

9-21.   Calculate the remaining sale prices for the items on Shirley's list. Can she afford to buy them all? If not, what should she leave off?

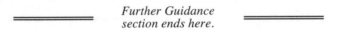

*Further Guidance
section ends here.*

9-22.   Shirley bought a pair of socks to match a new outfit. The original price of the socks was $8, but their tag said "$2 off." Find the percent discount for the socks. At this same discount rate, how much would she save on an item that was originally priced at $5? At $50?

9-23.   Janet wanted to go to a concert and the tickets cost $25 each. She found a website that advertised that customers could save $7 by purchasing them there. She wonders what percent of the original price she would be saving. She drew the diagram below to help her **visualize** the problem.

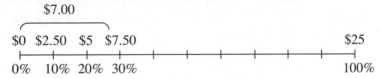

She could see from her diagram that $7.00 is somewhere between 20% and 30% of $25. Work with your team to help her figure out the exact percent.

9-24.   Craig looked at Janet's diagram and said, *"First, I think it will be useful for us to know what 1% of $25 is."*

a.   Discuss this with your team. Could it be useful to know 1% of $25? How?

b.   Find 1% of $25 and use this to help Janet solve her figure out what percent of $25 is $7.

9-25.   Janet redrew her diagram from problem 9-23 below to represent what she knows about the cost of her concert tickets.

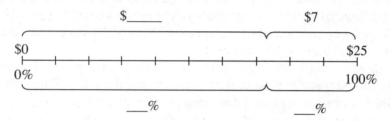

a.   Work with your team to fill in the missing information in Janet's diagram. Label each piece of information so that it is clear what it means in relation to Janet's concert tickets.

b.   Craig claimed that he could use Janet's diagram to answer any question that could be asked about the problem. His team was not so sure. They each wrote down a question to test Craig's claim. Can you find an answer to each of these questions by using Janet's diagram?

   i: Kara asked, *"What is the new cost of the concert tickets?"*

   ii: Penny asked, *"What percent of the original cost did she save by buying the tickets on the internet?"*

   iii: Paige followed with, *"What percent of the original cost did she pay for the Internet ticket?"*

9-26.   Janet decided to bring her brother with her to the concert. If she buys two tickets to the concert from the website, how much money will she save? What percent will she save? **Explain.**

9-27.   Kara liked Janet's diagram from problem 9-25. She said, *"I like that I can use this diagram to help check my work. I can add together the percent discount and the percent savings or I can find the sum of the new cost and the savings."*

Using your diagram from problem 9-25 discuss what Kara means, then write out a brief **explanation**.

9-28.   Shirley saw some other items that she liked while shopping at Dacy's. There was a bag that cost $26 and was marked at 10% off. She found a coupon in the paper for an additional 5% off the original price. Janet wondered, *"If an item is discounted 10% off the original price, then another 5% is also discounted from the original price, is that the same as 15% off?"* Work with your team to develop a convincing argument.

9-29.   Shirley wanted to buy a pair of boots that was originally priced at $100, but today Showy Shoes is advertising 20% off of everything in the store. She also has a coupon that promises 10% off of the price at the register. *"Great,"* she thinks. *"I will save 30% of $100, which means I will save $30."*

When she gets to the register, the cashier scans the tag on the boots and then scans her coupon. *"That will be $72, plus tax,"* she says.

Shirley is confused. When she left the store, she started the number lines below to help her figure out why the price was $72. Copy the number lines onto your own paper and work with your team to figure out why she was charged $72.

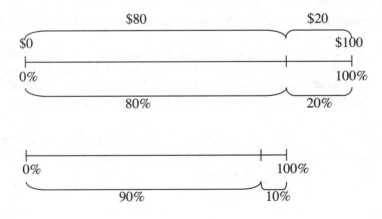

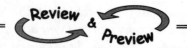

9-30.   Calculate the sale prices of each of the
         following discounted items.

   a.   A shirt originally priced at $30 has been
         discounted 20%.

   b.   A sofa originally priced at $1500 has
         been discounted 30%.

   c.   A loaf of bread originally priced at $3.49
         has been discounted 10%.

9-31.   Traniqua's assignment is to show how to divide $5 \div \frac{4}{5}$ using the Super
         Giant One.

   a.   Show what her work should look like.

   b.   Traniqua said, "I think I have an easy way to describe what we have been
         doing. For any problem where I need to divide a number (call it F) by a
         fraction $\frac{N}{D}$, I just multiply F by the reciprocal fraction $\frac{D}{N}$."

         Ahmal said, "Oh, my method works because the top of my super fraction is the
         same as Traniqua's and we know that the product of the denominators is always
         1 because of the number we choose for our Super Giant One. Let's just
         remember that it is 1 and that dividing by 1 does not change the answer. So we
         only need to worry about the numerators."

   c.   Make up two examples and use Traniqua's rule to do the divisions.

   d.   Traniqua had discovered a strategy that is sometimes called "Invert and
         Multiply." What does the word **invert** mean here, and what is inverted?

METHODS AND MEANINGS

Division by Fractions

Division of a Number by a Fraction using the Super Giant One Method:

The answer when you divide some number x by another number y is always $\frac{x}{y}$, but often we need to do some more work to make the answer into a number we recognize. For example,

$$6 \div \frac{3}{4} = \frac{6}{\frac{3}{4}} \cdot \frac{\frac{4}{3}}{\frac{4}{3}} = \frac{6 \cdot \frac{4}{3}}{1} = 6 \cdot \frac{4}{3} = \frac{24}{3} = 8$$

$$\frac{3}{4} \div \frac{2}{5} = \frac{\frac{3}{4}}{\frac{2}{5}} \cdot \frac{\frac{5}{2}}{\frac{5}{2}} = \frac{\frac{3 \cdot 5}{4 \cdot 2}}{1} = \frac{3}{4} \cdot \frac{5}{2} = \frac{15}{8}$$

Notice that in each case we used a super giant one that is made up of the inverted (flipped) denominator (bottom) of the fraction on both top and bottom. If we always make this choice, we will always get 1 when we multiply the two denominators together. Since any number divided by 1 is itself, the answer is just the numerator. In symbols,

$$F \div \frac{N}{D} = \frac{F}{\frac{N}{D}} \cdot \frac{\frac{D}{N}}{\frac{D}{N}} = \frac{F \cdot \frac{D}{N}}{1} = F \cdot \frac{D}{N} = \frac{F \cdot D}{N}$$

Division of Fractions with the Invert and Multiply Method:

$$F \div \frac{N}{D} = F \cdot \frac{D}{N}$$

Invert the divisor (switch the numerator and the denominator) and then multiply the fractions as usual.

$$\frac{3}{4} \div \frac{2}{5} = \frac{3}{4} \cdot \frac{5}{2} = \frac{15}{8}$$

9-32.   Find the sum $\frac{15}{2} + 0.28$ without a calculator.

9-33.   Kandi has a bag of marbles. She has 5 black, 3 white, 2 green, and 4 orange marbles. Kandi reaches into the bag without looking and pulls out a marble.

   a.   What is the probability that she will pull out a green marble?

   b.   If she does get a green marble and does not put it back in the bag, what is the probability she will now pull the other green marble from the bag?

   c.   Assume that Kandi does get the second green marble and does not return it to the bag. What is the probability she will now pull another green marble from the bag?

9-34.   Copy and complete each of the Diamond Problems below. The pattern used in the Diamond Problems is shown at right.

a.   b.   c.   d.

9.1.4 How does it grow?

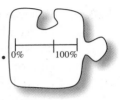

Simple Interest and Tips

It is often important when dealing with money to have strategies to calculate or estimate percents quickly and accurately. In this lesson, you will look at a variety of situations involving money in which percents are important. As you work with your team today, the following questions could help guide your discussions:

Is there another strategy that will work?

Is there a more efficient way?

Is the answer reasonable?

9-35.   WHAT IS THE TIP?

Kendra has three good friends who all have birthdays during the summer and every year she takes them out to dinner to celebrate. This year, the bill for dinner came to $125.

Kendra says, *"I never know how much money to leave as a tip."*

Rhonda replies, *"I always leave 15%."*

Then Shirley says, *"But our service was really good, I think we should leave 20%."*

a.   Without using a calculator, find two different ways to calculate the 15% tip that Rhonda thinks they should leave.

b.   Find two **different ways** to compute a 20% tip without using a calculator.

c.   Rhonda and Shirley were not able to convince one another as to how much of a tip to leave, so Kendra says, *"Let's compromise and leave an 18% tip."* Find two **different ways** to calculate the 18% tip that they will leave.

9-36.   Lorrayne's father wanted to teach Lorrayne about saving money. He offered to act as a bank and keep her money safe for her. He even said he would pay her 4% simple interest on her money for a year. In other words, if she gave him a sum of money, after one year, he would add 4% of that sum to her "account."

She told Jill and Jane about this and they went to their parents to propose similar plans. Below is information about the arrangement each girl made with her parents.

Lorrayne says, *"I gave my dad $1000 and he will pay 4% interest."*

Jill states, *"My mom offered to pay me 5.5% interest and I gave her my $800."*

Jane says, *"I gave my $950 to my parents. They will pay 4.5% interest."*

a.   After one year, how much interest will each girl have earned? Show your work.

b.   How much money will each girl have after one year?

9-37.   John wants to borrow $15 from Tyler. *"C'mon!"* says John. *"I'll make a deal with you. If you loan me the $15, I will pay it back to you with 35% interest next week. Or I'll pay you back the $15 and an extra $5. Your choice."*

If Tyler agrees to loan John the money, which deal will give Tyler more money in the end—the 35% interest or the extra $5? **Explain** your choice.

9-38.   Gina and Matt both arranged savings plans with their parents. Gina's parents promised to pay 8.5% interest. Matt's parents offered only 3% interest each year. When Gina heard about Matt's arrangement, she said, *"That means that I am going to have more money than you next year!"* Discuss Gina's comment with your team and **explain** whether you agree or disagree and why.

9-39.   LEARNING LOG

In a Learning Log entry, **describe** strategies for calculating percentages without a calculator. Be sure to include examples to demonstrate your thinking. Title this entry "Calculating Percentages Mentally" and label it with today's date.

Making Connections: Course 1

Methods and Meanings

MATH NOTES

Calculating Percents by Composition

Knowing quick methods to calculate 10% of a number and 1% of a number will help you to calculate other percents **by composition**.

$$10\% = \tfrac{1}{10}$$
$$1\% = \tfrac{1}{100}$$

To calculate 13% of 25, you can think of 10% of 25 + 3(1% of 25).

$$10\% \text{ of } 25 \Rightarrow \tfrac{1}{10} \text{ of } 25 = 2.5 \text{ and}$$
$$1\% \text{ of } 25 \Rightarrow \tfrac{1}{100} \text{ of } 25 = 0.25 \text{ so}$$
$$13\% \text{ of } 25 \Rightarrow 2.5 + 3(0.25) \Rightarrow 2.5 + 0.75 = 3.25$$

To calculate 19% of 4500, you can think of 2(10% of 4500) − 1% of 4500.

$$10\% \text{ of } 4500 \Rightarrow \tfrac{1}{10} \text{ of } 4500 = 450 \text{ and}$$
$$1\% \text{ of } 4500 \Rightarrow \tfrac{1}{100} \text{ of } 4500 = 45 \text{ so}$$
$$19\% \text{ of } 4500 \Rightarrow 2(450) - 45 \Rightarrow 900 - 45 = 855$$

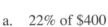

9-40.   Determine each of the following percentages without using a calculator. Show your work or **explain** your thinking for each problem.

a.   22% of $400

b.   19% of $35

c.   94% of $130

9-41.   Calculate the sale price of each of the following discounted items.

a.   A car originally priced at $15,500 is discounted 25%.

b.   A pair of shoes originally priced at $39 is discounted 15%.

9-42.   Let x represent the weight (in ounces) of one banana, y represent the weight of one peach, and z represent the weight of one "personal sized" watermelon. Jen placed bananas, peaches, and watermelons in her shopping basket while at the grocery store. The diagram below represents her selection of fruit.

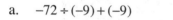

a.   According to the diagram, how many of each fruit did Jen place in her basket?

b.   Use the diagram to write a variable expression that represents the weight of the fruit she selected.

c.   If each banana weighs 5 ounces, each peach weighs 10 ounces, and each watermelon weighs 48 ounces, use the expression you created in part (b) to find the total weight of Jen's fruit.

9-43.   In the right prism shown in the diagram at right, the area of the base is 20 square feet. Find the volume of the prism.

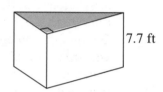

7.7 ft

9-44.   Simplify each of the following expressions without a calculator. Show your steps.

a. $-72 \div (-9) + (-9)$ b. $-72 \div (-9 + (-9))$

c. $-72 \div (-9) - (-9)$ d. $-80 \div 20 - 15 - (-5)$

Making Connections: Course 1

9.2.1 What is the relationship?

Distance, Rate, and Time

In this course you have looked at several relationships between two sets of information and investigated how one piece of information can or cannot be found from the other. In this section, you will look closely at an important family of relationships, called **proportional relationships**. You will learn to identify proportional relationships when you find them, and how to use your understanding of proportionality to solve problems.

To being your investigation of this special type of relationship, you will look at the mathematical relationship between distance, speed, and time.

9-45.   George stood on the train platform and waved goodbye to his sister who was going away for the summer. Just as he was getting in his car to drive home, he saw a light flashing inside the train station and heard an announcement that the train that carried his sister had malfunctioned and was stuck on the tracks. George had a map of the train's route and decided to drive to where the train was stuck and pick up his sister. How can he figure out where the train is? What information would help him to figure it out? Be prepared to share your ideas with the class.

9-46.   TOY CARS

Suppose you needed to predict how far a car, train, or plane had gone. It would be helpful to know something about how fast it was going and how long it had been moving. You will work with your team to Investigate the relationship between distance, speed (or rate), and time in the following experiment.

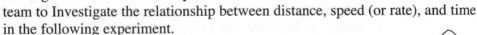

Obtain a meter stick, a toy car, a long piece of paper, and a stopwatch from your teacher. Put the paper on the floor, draw a starting line near one end of it, and place the car on the edge of the paper facing the starting line as shown at right. Place the car a little way behind the starting line so that it can reach a constant speed by the time it gets to the starting line.

Problem continues on next page →

9-46.   *Problem continued from previous page.*

Read the directions below for taking data *before* starting your car.

Directions for Taking Data
1. Appoint a Timer, a Car-starter, a Marker, and a Measurer.
2. The Car-starter should start the car.
3. As the front end of the car reaches the starting line, the Timer should start the stopwatch.
4. When one second has passed, the Timer calls out "Now" and the Marker makes a mark (without actually touching the car) at the place on the paper where the front end of the car was at that moment. This process repeats at two seconds, three seconds, etc. until the car has reached the end of the paper.
5. The Measurer measures each distance in centimeters *from the starting line*.

a. Run the experiment one time *without collecting data*, and talk with your team about how, exactly, you will take data.

b. Work with your team to take data **comparing** the time that has passed (in seconds) to the distance (in cm) that the car is from the starting line, following the directions above.

c. Obtain a Lesson 10.2.1 Resource Page from your teacher. Work with your team to organize your data into a table and graph it. Be prepared to share your table and graph with the class. Then think about the following questions.

i.   Should your graph "stop"? Would it **make sense** to continue your graph to show how your car would travel if you were to continue measuring for more time?

ii. How far would you expect your car to have traveled after 1.5 seconds have passed? What about after 1.25 seconds? Does it **make sense** to connect the points on the graph? Why or why not?

9-47.   Approximately how far does your car travel each second? How can you see this in your table? How can you see it on your graph? Be prepared to **explain** your ideas to the class.

9-48.   If your car were twice as fast, how far would it travel each second? How would you see this in the table? How would you see it on the graph? Again, be prepared to **explain** your ideas to the class.

9-49.   The distance your car has traveled and the time it has taken are related to each other **proportionally** (if your car travels at a constant speed). In a proportional relationship, two quantities are related with a constant multiplier. For your car, the constant multiplier can be called **rate** (or speed).

Where else in this course, have you seen two quantities related by a constant multiplier? Work with your team to come up with examples of proportional relationships and be ready to contribute your ideas to the class discussion.

9-50.   Answer each of the following questions and be ready to **explain** how you could use your table or graph to get each answer.

a.   What distance would your car travel in 9 seconds?

b.   How far would your car travel in 25 seconds?

c.   How many seconds would it take your car to travel 300 cm?

9-51.   Bella wants to use her new toy car to deliver a secret note to Edward, who is sitting all the way across the cafeteria, approximately 20 meters (2000 cm) from her. She plans to get the car started and then leave the cafeteria so Edward will not see her. If her car travels at 110 cm per second, about how much time will she have to get out before Edward gets the note?

9-52.   Which of the tables below shows a proportional relationship? How can you tell?

a.

1	2
2	4
3	6
4	8

b.

1	2
2	3
3	4
4	5

9-53.   **Additional Challenge:** Gloria and David's cars crossed the starting line at exactly the same time and are traveling in the same direction. Gloria's car travels at 40 centimeters per second and David's car travels 35 centimeters per second. After 20 seconds, how far apart will their cars be? Be prepared to **explain** your thinking to the class?

9-54.   It took Ivan 7 hours to drive 385 miles at a constant speed. How fast was he driving? Show how you know.

9-55.   Each problem below has an error in the answer. Find the error, **explain** how to correct the mistake, and correct it. In parts (a) and (d), the × means to multiply.

    a.   10   b.   467.92   c.   100
        × 0.5   +1.293   −62.837
         50   479.85   38.837

    d.   1.234   e.   4006.3   f.   45.6
        × 0.003   − 34.98   32.87
          0.3702   3971.48   + 0.003
                                                   374.6

9-56.   Determine each of the following percentages without using a calculator. Show your work or **explain** your thinking for each problem.

    a.   20% of $24   b.   30% of $24

    c.   5% of $24   d.   15% of $24

9-57.   Make a graph to show the relationship between distance and time for a bicycle that travels 10 miles every hour.

9-58.   Find the value of the variable that makes each equation true.

    a. $\frac{y}{3} = 10$ b. $w - 6 = -4$

9.2.2 How can I see a proportion?

Graphing Proportional Relationships

In the previous lesson, you learned that proportional relationships can be identified by finding a constant multiplier. In fact, you have seen relationships with constant multipliers several times in this course. Today, you will look back at a few of these earlier situations in which two sets of information are being **compared** that are related proportionally.

9-59.   GRAPHING THE PENNY TOWER DATA

In Chapter 1, you found a multiplicative (or proportional) relationship between the height of a stack of pennies and the number of pennies in the stack. That is, you could always find one piece of information by multiplying the other by a constant number.

Height of tower (cm)	# of Pennies
1	
15	
4	28
	63
3	
12	

a. Copy the table at right and work with your team to fill in the missing values. What strategies did you use to determine the missing numbers?

b. How many pennies are in a tower with a height of 0 cm? Add a row to your table with this value.

c. Graph this data. Be sure to scale the axes so that all of the points in your table are visible on your graph.

d. What do you notice about the graph of height and number of pennies? How does this graph **compare** to the graphs of time and distance that you made in Lesson 9.2.1? What do the graphs have in common? How are they different?

9-60.   BAGS O' BLOCKS

Although you may not have known the name it at the time, you worked with proportional relationships as you studied probability in Chapter 5. Consider this connection as you answer the questions below with your team.

Imagine that you have a bag with 12 blocks inside, five of which are blue.

a. Imagine that you chose a block from this bag at random, wrote down its color, and then replaced it. How many times would you expect to get a blue block for different numbers of draws? Work with your team to complete the table at right.

# of Draws	Expected # of Blue Blocks
0	
12	
24	
36	
60	
132	

b. Is there a proportional relationship between the number of draws and the number of times you would expect to get a blue block? That is, is there a multiplier to get the number of blue blocks from the number of draws? If so, how can you find it? If not, **explain** how you know.

c. Graph this data on graph paper. How does this graph **compare** the graph of the penny tower data from problem 9-59 and the graphs of distances cars traveled in certain amounts of time in Lesson 9.2.1? Does this graph show a proportional relationship? **Explain**.

d. How many blue blocks would you expect to have drawn after you have made each of the following numbers of draws? For each situation, **describe** your strategy for finding the answer.

   i.   300 draws?

   ii.   1200 draws?

   iii. 90 draws?

9-61. Rahim has some blocks in a bag. He knows how many blocks are there, and how many of them are red, but he does not want to tell you. Instead, he just shows you the graph at right.

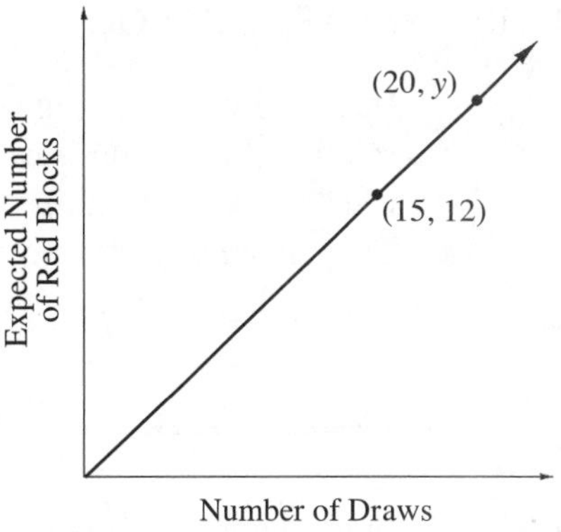

a. What does the point (15, 12) tell you about Rahim's blocks?

b. Assuming Rahim has drawn his graph correctly, what is the missing value of the second coordinate point, (20, y)? **Explain** how you know?

c. If you draw from Rahim's bag 50 times, how many times would you expect to get a red block?

d. How many blocks are in Rahim's bag? **Explain** how you know and be prepared to share your ideas with the class.

9-62. The following graphs show examples of relationships that are *not* proportional. For each graph, **explain** what makes the relationship different from the proportional relationships you have studied.

a.

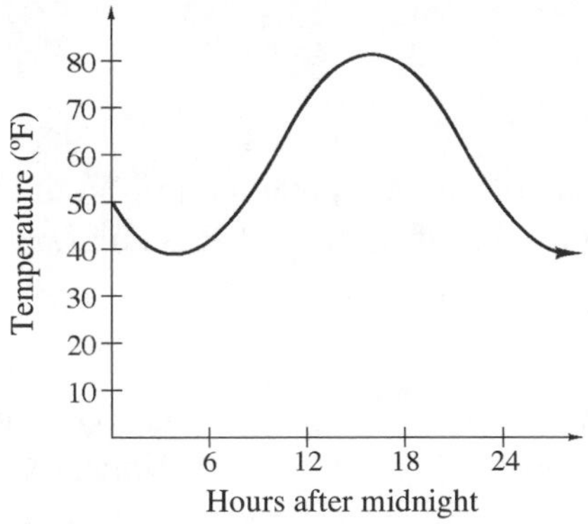

b.

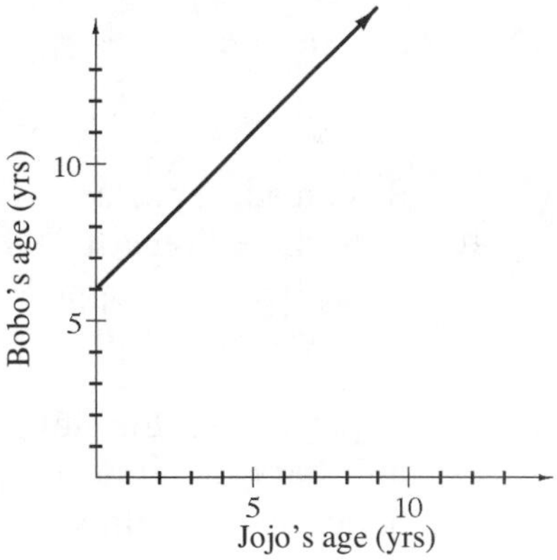

c.

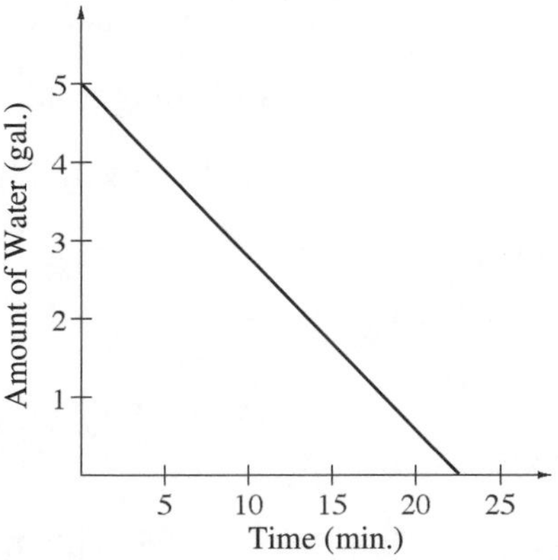

d.

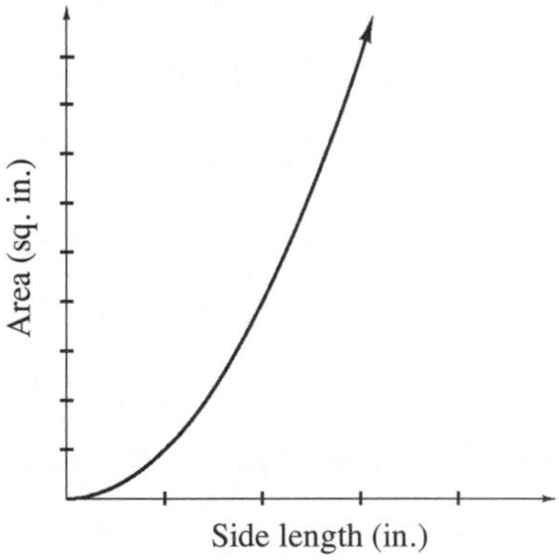

9-63.   LEARNING LOG

In your Learning Log, **explain** what a proportional
relationship is and how you can see it. Include diagrams to
illustrate your thinking and make an example of your own.
Title this entry "Proportional Relationships" and label it
with today's date.

9-64.   Find the area and perimeter of the figure at right. All
angles are right angles. Show your work.

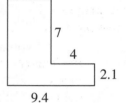

9-65.   Find the value of the variable that makes each
equation true.

a. $5a - 3 = 17$ b. $2x + 1 = -9$

9-66.   In a previous course you may have learned that $8^3 = 8 \cdot 8 \cdot 8 = 512$. Rewrite the
following expressions using multiplication and then calculate the final value for
each (as shown for 8^3 above).

a. 10^4 b. 5^3 c. $(\frac{1}{2})^2$ d. $(-2)^3$

9-67.   Rosa made a pizza, and half of the pizza has spinach on it. Four-fifths of the
spinach section also has pineapple. What portion of Rosa's pizza has both
spinach and pineapple?

9-68.   Depending on the situation, numbers may be exact or approximate. **Exact
numbers** are numbers from counting, mathematical relationships, definitions,
or decisions. **Approximate numbers** arise from measurement or rounding.

Tell whether the number in each sentence is exact or approximate.

a.   There are 12 inches in a foot.   b.   Sam's height is 157 centimeters.

c.   There are four books on the shelf.   d.   The driving age is 16 years old.

e.   It is 93,000,000 miles from the earth to the sun.

f.   With a tax rate of 8%, the tax on a $14.95 CD is $1.20.

9-69.   Simplify each of the following expressions.

a. $\frac{2}{3} + \frac{3}{4}$ b. $\frac{2}{3} \div \frac{3}{4}$ c. $1\frac{2}{3} \cdot 6$ d. $-1\frac{2}{3}(-6)$

Making Connections: Course 1

9.2.3 Is it proportional?

Identifying and Using Proportional Relationships

In this section you have discovered that for proportional relationships there is a multiplier you can use to find one quantity given the other (for example, you can find the number of pennies in a tower of pennies by multiplying the number of inches by seven). You have also seen that graphs of proportional relationships are straight lines that include the point $(0,0)$. Note that these kinds of proportional relationships are generally knows as **direct proportions**. Today, you will use your understanding of proportional relationships to solve problems.

9-70. In Chapter 8 you learned that graphs can be extended to include negative values, and you made a graph of all of the pairs of x and y values that make $\frac{x}{y}$ equivalent to $\frac{2}{5}$. A copy of the graph of $\frac{x}{y} = \frac{2}{5}$ is shown at right. (Note that $\frac{x}{y} = \frac{2}{5}$ and $y = \frac{2}{5}x$ represent the same thing except when $\frac{x}{y}$ is $\frac{0}{0}$.)

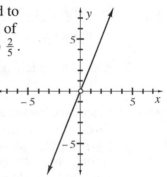

Your task: Work with your team to decide whether the relationship between x and y in $\frac{x}{y} = \frac{2}{5}$ is proportional. Be ready to contribute your ideas to the class discussion.

9-71. Kaci loves cheese and buys it whenever she can. Recently, she bought 5 pounds of swiss cheese for $15.00 and 3 pounds of gouda for $7.50.

a. Obtain a copy of the Lesson 9.2.3 Resource Page for each member of your team. Then work together to plot and label Kaci's two cheese purchases as two points on the graph provided.

b. With your team, find another point that you could plot on the graph for *each* kind of cheese. That is, find another combination of pounds of cheese and the associated cost for the swiss and then another combination of pounds and cost for the gouda.

c. Work with your team to discuss and answer the following questions. Then decide how best to complete the graph that you started in parts (a) and (b).

  • Can you find any other points that should be on the graph? Plot them.

  • Should the points on this graph be connected? If so, why does that **make sense?** If not, why not?

Problem continues on next page →

9-71.   *Problem continued from previous page.*

    d. How do the graphs for each type of cheese **compare**? What is the same and what is different?

    e. Which cheese is more expensive (costs more per pound)? How can you tell by looking at the graph?

9-72.   You have learned many strategies for finding unknown quantities in proportional relationships. Use your understanding of proportions to help Kaci find each of the missing quantities below, using the information given in problem 9-71. Be prepared to **explain** your strategies.

    a. How much does 7.5 pounds of swiss cheese cost?

    b. How much does 1.5 pounds of gouda cheese cost?

    c. How much swiss cheese can Kaci buy for $12?

    d. How much gouda cheese can Kaci buy for $10.

9-73.   On your own graph paper, draw axes, decide on a scale, and plot points to represent the data in the table at right. Does this data appear to be proportional? **Explain** why or why not.

Quantity x	Quantity y
2	7
6	21
9	31.5
5	17.5
1	3.5

9-74.   Simplify $4(\frac{5}{6}) + \frac{3}{4}$ and write your answer as a mixed number.

9-75.   Since $4^2 = 4 \cdot 4 = 16$, it follows that $3 \cdot 4^2 = 3 \cdot 4 \cdot 4 = 48$. Rewrite each expression without exponents and compute the value.

    a. 5^2 b. $2 \cdot 5^2$ c. 3^3 d. $2^2 \cdot 3^3$

9-76.   A bag contains 4 brown marbles, 3 green marbles, 2 red marbles, and 1 purple marble. Calculate the theoretical probability of drawing each color, and write each answer as a fraction, as a percent, and as a decimal.

9-77.   Write an equation for each diagram below and find the value of the variable.

    a. 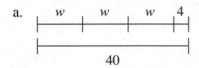   b.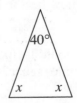

9.2.4 What is the missing number?

••

Finding Missing Information in Proportional Relationships

Since proportional relationships are those with a multiplier, it may be no surprise that a multiplication table could be used to help us solve problems involving proportions. Throughout this course, you have used patterns in the multiplication table to help solve different kinds of problems. In this lesson, all of these ideas will come together to uncover a new strategy for finding missing quantities in proportional relationships.

9-78.   Kaci was trying to figure out how many pounds of gouda cheese she could buy for $10, knowing that 3 pounds costs $7.50. She wrote the equivalent ratios below.

$$\frac{3 \text{ pounds}}{\$7.50} = \frac{x}{\$10}$$

Work with your team to brainstorm a list of all of the methods that you can think of that Kaci could use to find the information she is missing. Be prepared to share your ideas with the rest of the class.

9-79.   Consider the connections between these ideas and the multiplication table as you answer the questions below.

a.   In Chapter 1, you noticed a pattern involving the products of numbers at opposite corners of rectangles drawn on the table. For example, you **compared** the products $6 \cdot 35$ and $14 \cdot 15$, taken from the opposite corners of the rectangle drawn on the diagram at right.

	1	2	3	4	5	6
1	1	2	3	4	5	6
2	2	4	6	8	10	12
3	3	6	9	12	15	18
4	4	8	12	16	20	24
5	5	10	15	20	25	30
6	6	12	18	24	30	36
7	7	14	21	28	35	42

Work with your team to recall what you found and to test some other rectangles until you are convinced that the pattern is consistent. b.   Why does this pattern work? Work with your team to **explain** why it **makes sense** that the products of opposite corners of *any* rectangle in the multiplication table are equal.

Problem continues on next page →

9-79.   *Problem continued from previous page.*

    c.   You have also used the multiplication table to help you see equivalent fractions (and ratios). What are the equivalent fractions or ratios that are represented by the corners of the rectangle in the above diagram?

    d.   How can you use the pattern that you have found for the products of diagonals to find missing information in a pair of equivalent fractions or ratios such as the problem below?

$$\frac{5}{15} = \frac{x}{24}$$

    e.   Would this method of using the products of opposite corners (also called finding **cross-products**) to find a missing piece of information work for numbers that are *not* on your multiplication table? That is, what if the numbers are larger than or in between those on the table? What if they were negative numbers? Would the method still work? Discuss these questions with your team and **explain** what you have decided and why.

9-80.   Work with your team to use cross products to help Kaci figure out the amount of cheese she could buy for $10. Her equivalent ratios are reprinted below.

$$\frac{3 \text{ pounds}}{\$7.50} = \frac{x}{\$10}$$

9-81.   Find the missing information in each set of equivalent ratios below, using any method. Be sure that you record your process so that others can see what you did.

    a. $\frac{2}{15} = \frac{x}{5}$ b. $\frac{x}{100} = \frac{7}{8}$ c. $\frac{0.2}{2} = \frac{1}{x}$ d. $\frac{y}{11.2} = \frac{4}{7}$

9-82.   LEARNING LOG

In this section, you have used a number of different strategies for finding missing information in proportional relationships.

In your Learning Log, show each of these methods. Include examples to show your thinking. Title this entry "Methods for Finding Missing Information in Proportional Relationships" and label it with today's date.

MATH NOTES

METHODS AND MEANINGS

Proportional Relationship

Two quantities are in a (direct) proportional relationship if the value of one of them is always the same multiple of the value of the other. In algebraic terms, we write $y = Kx$ or $\frac{y}{x} = K$, where K is the constant of proportionality.

For example, if a car drives at a constant speed of 60 miles per hour, the amount of time that the car has been driving (x) and the distance it has traveled (y), are related proportionally. For a 3 hour trip, $x = 3$ (hrs), $K = 60$ (miles per hour) and $y = 180$ (miles).

Another example would be if the sales tax rate is 8%, the cost of an item (x) and the amount of tax you need to pay (y) are related proportionally. For a \$40 item, $x = \$40$, $K = 8\% = 0.08$, and $y = \$3.20$.

Review & Preview

9-83. Find the missing value in each of the pairs of equivalent ratios below.

a. $\frac{x}{10} = \frac{6}{15}$

b. $\frac{12}{9} = \frac{8}{x}$

c. $\frac{16}{38} = \frac{200}{m}$

9-84. Use correct order of operations to simplify each expression.

a. $10 \cdot \frac{1}{2} + (-6)(-3)$

b. $\dfrac{-5 + -6(\frac{2}{3})}{-3}$

9-85. Evaluate the expressions below using $r = 3$ and $h = 5$.

a. $6h - 4$

b. $8r + h$

c. r^2

9-86.   State whether the number in each sentence is exact or approximate.

a.   The voting age is 18 years old.

b.   For a circle of radius 2 inches, the area is 12.56 square inches.

c. $4^3 = 64$.

d.   The length of my pencil is 10.25 centimeters.

e.   I put 2 tablespoons of chocolate syrup on my ice cream.

9-87.   Convert each fraction to an equivalent decimal rounded to the nearest hundredth.

a. $\frac{2}{3}$ b. $\frac{7}{8}$ c. $\frac{1}{9}$

9.2.5 What is the multiplier?

Circumference, Diameter, and Pi

You have found *so many* proportional relationships! Did you realize that they were so numerous? In future math courses, you will discover that there are many other types of relationships that are *not* proportional. Today, however, you will investigate one more, very important proportional relationship: the ratio of circumference to diameter in circles.

9-88.   Imagine a regularly sized can of tennis balls.* If you were to wrap a string around the can and cut it so that it does not overlap and then stretch the same piece of string along the can's length, how would the length of string **compare** to the length of the can? Would it be shorter than the can? Longer? The same length? Discuss this with your team and make a prediction. (*This problem is adapted from the work of Marilyn Burns.)

9-89.   BUBBLE MADNESS

The idea of **circumference** of a circle is similar to the idea of perimeter for other shapes; it is the distance around the circle. Wrapping a string around a circular object is one way to measure its circumference. In this activity, you will investigate the relationship of the circumference of a circle to its **diameter** (length from one side of the circle to the other, through its center).

a.   Follow the directions below.

- Obtain a bubble wand, some bubble solution, and construction paper from your teacher.

- Blow a bubble and allow it to land and pop on your construction paper. You will see a circle on your paper. (If this does not produce a clear circle, try catching the bubble you blow with your bubble wand and then placing it on the construction paper.)

Problem continues on next page →

9-89.   *Problem continued from previous page.*

      • Wrap a string carefully around this circle and then stretch it along a meter stick to measure the **circumference** of the circle, accurate to the nearest tenth of a centimeter.

      • Then use a ruler or string to find the longest measurement across the circle. This is the **diameter**.

      Share tasks so that each person has a chance to blow some bubbles and to measure their circumference and diameter. Take data for at least 8 circles of different sizes.

    b. Organize your data in a table and then work with your team to decide on an appropriate scale. Then graph the data carefully on your own paper.

9-90.   Does the relationship between circumference and diameter appear to be proportional? (Remember that these are measurements and will thus have some degree of error.) If this relationship appears to be proportional, approximately what is the multiplier between the diameter and the circumference?

9-91.   If the diameter of a bubble is 9 cm, can you approximate its circumference without measuring it? Justify your answer in as **many ways** as you can.

9-92.   The ratio of circumference to diameter for circles has been measured to greater and greater accuracy since before 1650 B.C. The ratio has been found to be equal to π (spelled in English *pi* and pronounced "pie"), which is an **irrational number** (there is no way to write it as a fraction with integers) slightly larger than 3. Find the button marked "π" on your calculator.

    a. Write down the decimal equivalent for π, accurate to the nearest hundredth.

    b. The fraction $\frac{22}{7}$ is often used to approximate π. What is the decimal equivalent of $\frac{22}{7}$, accurate to the nearest hundredth?

9-93.   Work with your team to generalize the relationship between circumference and diameter of a circle. In other words, **describe** how you could calculate the circumference of any circle if you knew the diameter and how you could find the length of the diameter if you knew the circumference.

9-94.   Now return to your prediction from problem 9-88. Discuss it with your team again. Has your prediction changed? Why or why not? Work with your team to test your prediction.

9-95.   Scientists have measured the diameter of the earth at the equator to be about 7926 miles. If you were to travel all the way around the earth along the equator, approximately how many miles would you have traveled?

   Additional Challenge 1: If it takes the average human two hours to walk five miles, how long would it take a person to walk around the earth (assuming it were possible).

   Additional Challenge 2: Signals that travel across the Internet are often carried through fiber-optic cables and travel at the speed of light (approximately 186,000 miles every second). At this rate, how long would it take an email to travel around the earth?

9-96.   LEARNING LOG

   Write a Learning Log entry summarizing what you learned about circumference and its relationship to the diameter of a circle. Title this entry "Circumference and Diameter" and label it with today's date.

METHODS AND **M**EANINGS

MATH NOTES

Solving Proportions

An equation stating that two ratios are equal is called a **proportion**. Some examples of proportions are:

$$\frac{5}{7} = \frac{50}{70}$$

$$\frac{6\,mi}{2\,hr} = \frac{9\,mi}{3\,hr}$$

When two ratios are known to be equal, setting up a proportion is one strategy for solving for an unknown part of one ratio. For example, if the ratios $\frac{9}{2}$ and $\frac{x}{16}$ are equal, setting up the proportion $\frac{x}{16} = \frac{9}{2}$ allows you to solve for x.

Strategy 1: One way to solve this proportion is by using a Giant One to find the equivalent ratio. In this case, since the scale factor between 2 and 16 is 8, we create the Giant One,

$$\frac{x}{16} = \frac{9}{2} \boxed{\frac{8}{8}} = \frac{9 \cdot 8}{2 \cdot 8} = \frac{72}{16} \quad \text{so} \quad x = 72$$

Strategy 2: Use Cross Multiplication. This is a solving strategy for proportions that is based on the process of multiplying each side of the equation by the denominators of each ratio and setting the two sides equal.

Complete Algebraic Solution

$$\frac{x}{16} = \frac{9}{2}$$

$$2 \cdot 16 \cdot \frac{x}{16} = \frac{9}{2} \cdot 2 \cdot 16$$

$$2 \cdot x = 9 \cdot 16$$

$$2x = 144$$

$$x = 72$$

Cross Multiplication

$$\frac{x}{16} = \frac{9}{2}$$

$$\frac{x}{16} \diagup\kern-0.9em\diagdown \frac{9}{2}$$

$$2 \cdot x = 9 \cdot 16$$

$$2x = 144$$

$$x = 72$$

9-97.   Find the missing value in each of the following proportions.

  a. $\frac{x}{12} = \frac{12}{18}$ b. $\frac{4}{5} = \frac{m}{45}$ c. $\frac{11}{40} = \frac{p}{100}$

9-98.   The Minneapolis and Denver airports are 693 miles apart. If an airplane can fly between the two cities in 2.1 hours, how fast is the airplane traveling? Show how you know.

9-99.   Five pounds of fertilizer is needed for 1000 square feet of garden. To calculate how much fertilizer should be used for a 450 square foot garden Alex wrote this proportion: $\frac{5\ lbs}{1000\ ft^2} = \frac{n\ lbs}{450\ ft^2}$.

  a.   Solve this proportion for n.

  b.   Solve this problem using a similar proportion. Juan makes four out of every nine shots he takes in basketball. At the same rate, how many shots will he make if he shoots 135 times?

9-100.   Autumn and her friends had dinner at their favorite restaurant and the bill came to $60. They decided to leave 18% of the bill for a tip. Without a calculator, help them compute how much money is 18% of the bill.

9-101.   Find the area and perimeter of the rectangle below. Show your work.

$1\frac{5}{6}$ in.

$4\frac{1}{2}$ in.

9-102.   Estimate the circumference or diameter for each of the following circles. For each one, give your reasoning.

  a.   The diameter is 1 cm. What is the circumference?

  b.   The diameter is 7.2 meters. What is the circumference?

  c.   The circumference is 1 mile. What is the diameter?

  d.   The circumference is 12 inches. What is the diameter?

9-103.   Jack has 120 songs on his MP3 player. Some are rock, some are jazz, and the rest are classical pieces. If his MP3 player is on random shuffle mode, the probability it will play a classical piece is $\frac{2}{5}$ and the probability it will play a jazz piece is $\frac{1}{3}$. How many songs of each type are on Jack's MP3 player?

9-104.   Estimate the value of each of the following expressions and **explain** your reasoning. Then check your estimations by calculating them.

    a. $\frac{4}{5} + \frac{7}{8}$ b. $\frac{7}{8} - \frac{3}{4}$ c. $\frac{4}{9} \cdot \frac{6}{10}$ d. $\frac{2}{3} \div \frac{5}{6}$

9-105.   If baseball were played on Mars, the balls would fly much farther than they do on Earth. One could then speculate that the number of home runs hit would be much greater on Mars. Mike expects that he would hit 50% more home runs if he were playing baseball on Mars. If he hit 76 homers on Earth, how many home runs does he expect he would hit on Mars?

9-106.   Copy the number line shown below and label the following numbers at their approximate place on the number line.

$$\overset{\displaystyle 0 \hspace{5.5cm} 1}{\longleftarrow\!\!\!\!|\rule{5.5cm}{0.4pt}|\!\!\!\!\longrightarrow}$$

    a. $\frac{1}{7}$ b.   65%   c.   0.87   d. $\frac{8}{9}$

9.3.1 How can I calculate area?

Area of Triangles

In Chapter 3, you learned how to calculate the area of rectangles and how to estimate area using square units. In this lesson, you will learn how to calculate the area of a triangle.

9-107. **HOW DO THEY COMPARE?**

Obtain a Lesson 9.3.1 Resource Page from your teacher. Cut out each of the triangles on the page and label the bolded side of each triangle "base." Then work with your team to investigate relationships among the triangles. Specifically, make a list of all of the ways in which they are the same and the ways in which they are different. Be prepared to share your findings with the class.

Discussion Points

What can we measure on each triangle?

How are they the same?

How are they different?

Further Guidance

9-108. Measure the **base** (one side of the triangle – in this case use the bold side) and **height** (the perpendicular distance from the base – or a line containing the base – to the point where the other two sides meet) of each of your triangles and record your data in a table such as the one at right.

Base	Height	

To measure the height, place the base along the lower edge of the height ruler. Then use the height ruler to measure the perpendicular distance from the base to the highest point of the triangle. In other words the height should be measured at a right angle to the base. You may have to slide your height ruler beyond the end of the base to do this in some cases.

9-109. Estimate the area of each triangle by counting square units. Add this information to the table you created in problem 9-108.

————   *Further Guidance*   ————
section ends here.

9-110. HOW CAN WE CALCULATE AREA?

Work with your team to write a conjecture about how you can calculate the area of a triangle if you know its base and height. When you have made a conjecture, test it by following the directions in parts (a) through (c) below.

a. On grid paper, use a straight edge to draw at least four different triangles. Label each triangle with its base and height.

b. Use your conjecture to calculate the area of each triangle.

c. Estimate the area of each triangle by counting square units using the grid.

d. Does your conjecture appear to be correct? Be prepared to share your ideas and your results with the class.

9-111. ANOTHER WAY

Use Triangles B and C from the Lesson 9.3.1 Resource Page and arrange them into a rectangle. What is the area of this rectangle? Show how you can calculate the area of each triangle based on the area of the rectangle.

9-112. JaMarcus has drawn a triangle with a base of 10 units and a height of 5 units.

a. What do you know about JaMarcus's triangle? Can you draw it?

b. What if JaMarcus told you that his triangle was a right triangle? Draw one possibility for his triangle. Are there others? Be prepared to **explain** your ideas to the class.

9-113. LEARNING LOG

What do you need to know about a triangle in order to calculate its area? Discuss this idea with your team and then record your ideas in your Learning Log. Title this entry "Area of a Triangle" and label it with today's date.

9-114.   Calculate the area of each triangle described below.

a.   Base: 6 cm, Height: 8 cm   b.   Base: 4 inches, Height: 3 inches

9-115.   Find the circumference of each of the circles described below.

a.   Radius of 3 inches   b.   Diameter of 27 cm.

9-116.   A pair of shoes originally costs \$42 but is on sale for 33% off. What is the new price? Show how you know.

9-117.   Multiple Choice: Which fraction below is equivalent to $\frac{7}{8}$? **Explain** how you can tell.

A. $\frac{9}{10}$ B. $\frac{14}{8}$ C. $\frac{49}{56}$ D. $\frac{49}{64}$

9-118.   Without a calculator, simplify each of the following expressions.

a. $0.25 + 2.5 + 2.5$ b. $432.7 - 0.08$

c. $4.57 \cdot 0.3$

9-119.   Copy and complete each of the Diamond Problems below. The pattern used in the Diamond Problems is shown at right.

a.   b.   c.   d.

9.3.2 How can I calculate area?

Area of Circles

In the previous lesson you explored areas of triangles. In this lesson, you will apply your understanding of area to circles. Recall, your study of circles in this course began in Chapter 9, when you found the relationship between the circumference of a circle and its diameter.

9-120.   Work with your team to write down everything you can remember that you have learned about circles. Be prepared to share your ideas with the class.

9-121.   CIRCLES AND SQUARES

Obtain a Lesson 9.3.2 Resource Page from your teacher. You will see two diagrams of the same circle with radius r. In the first diagram, you will see a dashed square that touches the circle at four points and lies outside of the circle. In the second diagram, you will see a dashed square that touches the circle at the same four points, but lies inside of the circle.

Your task: Work with your team to write an expression using r to represent the areas of each of the dashed squares. How do each of these areas relate to the area of the circle?

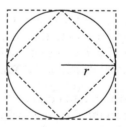

Discussion Points

How can we break the square into parts?

What dimensions can we figure out?

Making Connections: Course 1

Further Guidance

9-122. **CIRCLES IN SQUARES**

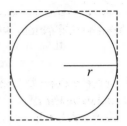

Examine a portion of the diagram, in which the circle lies inside of a dashed square. This portion is shown in the diagram at right.

a. On your resource page, draw a line from the center of the circle to the highest point on the circle. What is the length of this line?

b. Notice that in drawing this line, you have formed a small square. What is the area of this square?

c. Draw two more radii, one to connect the center of the circle with the lowest point and the other to the left-most point on the circle. Use the small squares you have formed to calculate the area of the large dashed square.

d. How does the area of the circle **compare** to the area of the large dashed square? Use this **comparison** to write a mathematical statement about the area of the circle.

9-123. **SQUARES IN CIRCLES**

Now examine a different portion of the diagram, in which the dashed square lies inside the circle, reprinted at right.

a. On your resource page, draw a line from the center of the circle to the highest point on the circle. Label this line with its length. Notice that there is now a triangle in the upper right portion of the figure. What is the area of this triangle?

b. Draw two more radii, one to connect the center of the circle with the lowest point and the other to the left-most point on the circle. Use the small triangles you have formed to calculate the area of the small dashed square.

c. How does the area of the circle **compare** to the area of the small dashed square? Use this **comparison** to write a mathematical statement about the area of the circle.

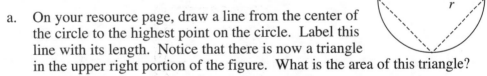

*Further Guidance
section ends here.*

9-124.   Estimate how many radius squares (squares with side-length r) fit inside each circle. Use this to write an expression for the approximate area of a circle.

9-125.   Remember π, the ratio of a circle's circumference to its diameter? It turns out that this special number also relates to the area of a circle. It is the ratio of a circle's area to the square of its radius. In other words, for a circle, $\pi = \frac{A}{r^2}$, so $A = \pi r^2$. Use this formula to calculate the area of each circle described below.

   a.   A circle with a radius of 2 meters.

   b.   A circle with a diameter of 10 miles.

9-126.   LEARNING LOG

   In your Learning Log, **explain** the meaning of the number π and how to use it to help calculate the area of a circle. Title this entry, "π and the Area of a Circle" and label it with today's date.

MᴇᴛHODS AND MᴇᴀNINGS

Area of Triangles

The area of a triangle can be calculated using the formula

$$A = \tfrac{1}{2} bh$$

where b is the length of the **base** of the triangle (one side) and h is the **height** (perpendicular distance from the base or the line through the base to the point where the other two sides of the triangle meet). Note that, unless the triangle is a right triangle, the height *is not* one of the sides of the triangle.

The triangle at right has a base of 10 units and a height of 2 units. The area can be calculated by:

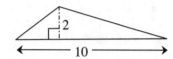

$A = \tfrac{1}{2}(10)(2) = 10$ square units.

The second triangle at right has a base of 6 units and a height of 7 units. The area can be calculated by:

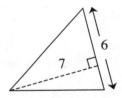

$A = \tfrac{1}{2}(6)(7) = 21$ square units.

The third triangle at right has a base of 6 units and a height of 5 units. This example illustrates when the height is drawn "to a line through the base" so that it will be perpendicular to that line.

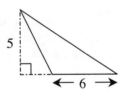

The area can be calculated by:

$A = \tfrac{1}{2}(6)(5) = 15$ square units.

9-127.   Find the area of each of the circles described below.

a.   A circular mirror with a radius of 3 centimeters.

b.   A circular dinner plate with a diameter of 9 inches.

9-128.   Calculate the area of each triangle described below.

a.   Base: 10 feet, Height: 6 feet   b.   Base: 14 mm, Height: 5 mm

9-129.   Assuming that the pattern continues, find the next three numbers in the sequence $-1, 2, 5, 8$. **Explain** how you know what the numbers should be.

9-130.   In the right prism shown at right, the area of the base is 42.5 square meters. Find the volume of the prism.

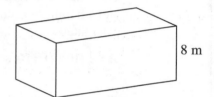

8 m

9-131.   Simplify each of the following expressions.

a. $\frac{1}{2} + \frac{2}{3} + \frac{1}{6}$ b. $1\frac{2}{3} - \frac{5}{12}$

9-132.   Two angles combine to form a straight line. One of the angles measures 25°. What is the measure of the other angle? Show or **explain** how you found your answer.

9.3.3   What is the area?

Area of Composite Shapes

In this lesson, you will consolidate your understanding of area as you find areas of complicated shapes. As you work on the problems in this lesson, ask your team members the following questions:

> How can we break this up into shapes that we can find the areas of?
>
> Is there **another way** to see it?
>
> Can we see the total area as a sum of areas? As a difference of areas?

9-133.   Shakira is planning to put a lawn in her backyard by installing sod (rolls of lawn) and she needs to know how many square feet of sod she should order. Her yard is irregularly shaped and has a fishpond in the center. The dimensions of the lawn she is planning are shaded in the diagram below. All measurements are in feet.

Your task: Obtain a Lesson 9.3.3A Resource Page from your teacher and work with your team to make a recommendation for how much sod Shakira should order. Can you find **more than one way** to calculate the area of Shakira's lawn?

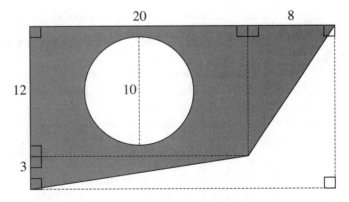

9-134. Copy each of the following shapes onto your own paper and calculate the areas of the regions formed with solid lines in as many ways as you can. What is the name of each shape?

a.

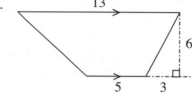

b.

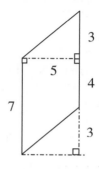

9-135. Gina designs and makes her own clothes. She drew the diagram at right (and also on the Lesson 9.3.3B Resource Page) of the fabric she needs for the front and back of a new shirt. If each unit on the grid represents one inch, how much fabric will she need?

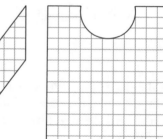
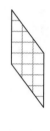

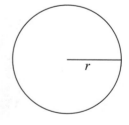

ETHODS AND MEANINGS

MATH NOTES

Area of Circles and π

For any circle with a diameter, d, and a circumference, c, the number π, one of the most important in mathematics, is defined as $\pi = \frac{c}{d} \approx 3.14$ where the ratio does not depend on the circle used.

If r is the radius of the circle, then the diameter and radius are related by $d = 2r$.

The area, A, of a circle can be calculated using the formula $A = \pi r^2$.

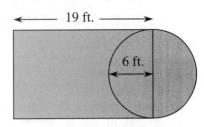

9-136.   Find the area of the part of a typical basketball court shaded in the diagram at right.

9-137.   Draw a parallelogram with a base of 3 cm and a height of 7 cm and show how to calculate its area.

9-138.   Find the area of the circles with dimensions given below.

a.   radius: 4 ft.   b.   diameter: 0.6 cm

9-139.   **Unit price** is the defined as the cost of one unit of an item. Suppose a 16 ounce bottle of shampoo costs $3.68. One way to find the unit price, that is, the price of one ounce of shampoo, is to write a proportion such as the one shown below.

$$\frac{\$3.68}{16 \text{ oz.}} = \frac{\$x}{1 \text{ oz.}}$$

Solving the proportion gives $x = \$0.23$, so this shampoo costs $0.23 per ounce.

a.   Find the unit price of *Italy* olive oil, which costs $2.90 for 10 ounces.

b.   Find the unit price of *Delicious* olive oil, which costs $4.96 for 16 ounces.

c.   If both brands are the same quality, which one is the better buy?

9-140.   **Unit rate** is defined as rate with a denominator of 1 unit. If a sprinter runs 100 meters in 10.49 seconds, her speed per second can be calculated as shown below. (Note that this was the world record set in 1988 by Florence Griffith-Joyner at the US Olympic Trials.)

$\frac{100 \ m}{10.49 \ sec} = \frac{x \ m}{1 \ sec}$ gives $x = 9.53$, so she ran 9.53 meters each second. This is a unit rate.

In addition, the number of seconds it takes her to run each meter can be calculated as $\frac{10.49 \ sec}{100 \ m} = \frac{x \ sec}{1 \ m}$ gives $x = 0.1049$, so it took her 0.1049 seconds to run each meter.

a.   An ice skater covered 1500 meters in 106.43 seconds. Find his unit rate of speed in meters per second.

b.   A train in Japan can travel 813.5 miles in 5 hours. Find the unit rate of speed in miles per hour.

c.   Alaska has a very low population density. It only has 655,000 people in 570,374 square miles. Find the unit rate of density in terms of people per square mile.

d.   New Jersey has a very high population density. It has 1,171 people per square mile. If Alaska had the same population density as New Jersey, what would be the population of Alaska? Solve with a proportion. (By the way, there were about 307,000,000 people in the United States as of the year 2009.)

9.3.4 How much can it hold?

Volume of Prisms and Cylinders

In this lesson, you will connect your new knowledge of circles with what you have learned about volume and prisms. You will figure out how to calculate the volume of a cylinder and a prism with triangular bases.

9-141. Obtain a Lesson 9.3.4 Resource Page from your teacher. Work with your team to cut out each of the grids. Each grid measures 12 cm by 5 cm.

a. With the first grid, build the vertical walls of a square-based prism. Your prism should be 5 cm high. Sketch the base of this prism on your paper. What are its dimensions? What is its area?

b. With the second grid, build a triangle-based prism. Again, your prism should be 5 cm high. The base should have sides of 3, 4, and 5 units. Sketch the base of this prism on your paper. What is its area?

c. With the third grid, build a **cylinder**, which is like a prism with a circular base. Your cylinder should be 5 cm high. Sketch the base of this cylinder on your paper. What is its radius? What is its area?

d. Find the volume of each of the prisms you have built. Then make a conjecture about the volume of the cylinder. Be prepared to **explain** your reasoning to the class.

9-142. Work with your class to test your conjecture about the volume of the cylinder. Note that one cubic centimeter (often shortened to cc) is equivalent to one milliliter (ml).

9-143.   DIGGING A POND

Mitch wants to put a fishpond in his back yard.
His parents have agreed, but have made the
following conditions:

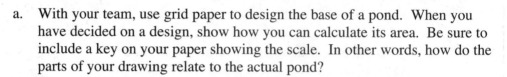

- *The walls of the pond must be vertical.*

- *The depth of the water must be the same in
  all parts of the pond.*

- *The pond must use no more than 350 cubic feet
  of water.*

a.   With your team, use grid paper to design the base of a pond. When you
     have decided on a design, show how you can calculate its area. Be sure to
     include a key on your paper showing the scale. In other words, how do the
     parts of your drawing relate to the actual pond?

b.   Decide on the depth of your pond. Show how you can be sure that your
     pond satisfies the volume restriction.

c.   Be ready to present your plan for a pond to the class.

9-144.   Now it is time to buy fish! Mitch wants Goldfish and Koi. The pet store has
         advised Mitch to allow 9 cubic feet of water for each Goldfish and 27 cubic feet
         of water for each Koi. How many of each fish can Mitch buy to fill the pond
         you have designed? Is there **more than one** possible solution? List as many
         combinations as you can find.

9-145.   LEARNING LOG

In your Learning Log, **explain** how to calculate the
volume of a cylinder. How is the volume similar to the
volume of a prism? Include examples to demonstrate your
thinking. Title this entry "Volume of a Cylinder" and
label it with today's date.

MᴇᴛHODS AND MᴇᴀNINGS

MATH NOTES

Prisms, Cylinders, and Their Volumes

A (right) **prism** is a three-dimensional figure composed of polygonal faces (called sides or lateral sides) and two **congruent** (same size and shape) parallel faces called bases. No holes are permitted in this solid. The remaining faces are rectangles. A prism is named for the shape of its bases. For example, the solid at right would be called a "square-based prism."

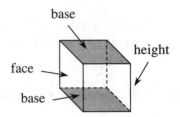

A (right) **circular cylinder** is a solid figure much like a prism except its bases are circles and the lines that join the bases are perpendicular to both of them. The **height** of a cylinder is the distance between the bases.

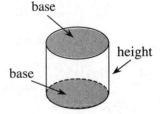

The formula for the volume, V, of either a prism or a cylinder is the same:

$$V = (\text{area of base}) \cdot (\text{height})$$

For a cylinder, this is the same as $V = (\pi r^2)h$.

9-146. Calculate the volume of the cylinder pictured at right.
        Round your answer to the nearest tenth.

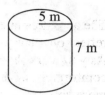

9-147. Draw a diagram of a box with a height of 6 inches, a width of 4 inches and a
        depth of 2 inches and then calculate its volume. Show all of your work.

9-148. Find a value of x that would make each equation true. Show all of your work.

        a. $19 = 3x + 7$ b. $37 - x = 16$

9-149. Consider this data: 22, 15, 30, 51, 27, 33, 19.

        a.   Arrange the data into a stem and leaf plot. .

        b.   Find the mean, median, and mode.

        c.   If the 51 were replaced with 33, which measures of central tendency would
             change and which would not? **Explain**.

9-150. Calculate each unit rate.

        a.   Misty typed 1104 words in 18 minutes. Find her rate of words per minute.

        b.   Hannah earned $134.75 in 11 hours. Find her rate of dollars per hour.

        c.   Six busses carried a total of 192 students. Find the rate of students per bus.

Chapter 9 Closure   What have I learned?

Reflection and Synthesis

The activities in chapter closure offer you a chance to reflect on what you have learned during this chapter. As you work, look for concepts that you feel very comfortable with, ideas that you would like to learn more about, and topics you need more help with. Look for connections among ideas as well as connections with material you learned previously.

①   SUMMARIZING MY UNDERSTANDING

This section gives you the opportunity to show what you know about proportional relationships.

Is it Proportional?

Obtain a GO page from your teacher, also available at www.cpm.org.

Your task, part 1: Work with your team to determine if the relationship between the height of a prism and its volume is or is not proportional. **Explain** your reasoning in **multiple ways**, being sure to include a table and a graph.

Your task, part 2: Work with your team to brainstorm relationships between quantities other than those you have seen in this chapter. Which ones might be proportional? Choose one relationship and demonstrate, using **multiple** reasons, whether it is or is not proportional. Again, be sure to include a table and a graph in your **explanation**.

Solving the problems in this section will help you to evaluate which types of problems you feel comfortable with and which you need more help with.

Solve each problem as completely as you can. The table at the end of this closure section provides answers to these problems. It also tells you where you can find additional help and practice on problems like these.

CL 9-151. Compute each of the following portions:

    a.   20% of 57   b.   85% of 17

CL 9-152. A ski parka that usually costs $85 is on sale for 25% off. What is the sale price?

CL 9-153. Robert took his family out to dinner to celebrate his recent promotion. The bill was $65. If he wants to leave a 15% tip, how much total money should he leave for the server?

CL 9-154. Mel's Grocery is selling three cans of soup for $5. Use this information to complete the table at right and graph the relationship between the number of cans you could buy and the price.

Cans	Price (in dollars)
0	0
3	5
6	
	15
30	
	45

CL 9-155. Solve each of the following proportions.

    a. $\frac{x}{24} = \frac{30}{36}$ b. $\frac{5}{7} = \frac{x}{3}$

    c.   If Joan read 75 pages in 4 hours how long will it take her to read 250 pages?

CL 9-156. Calculate the circumference of a circle with a radius of 14 cm.

CL 9-157. Calculate the area of each figure shown in the diagrams below.

    a.   b.

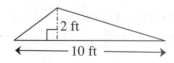

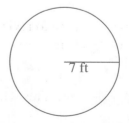

CL 9-158. Calculate the volume of each figure

a.

8.9 in.

3 in.

5 in.

b.

8 cm

10 cm

CL 9-159. For each of the problems above, do the following:

- Draw a bar or number line that represents 0 to 10.

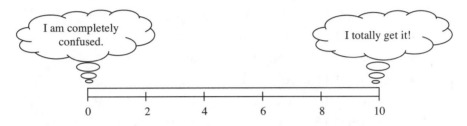

- Color or shade in a portion of the bar that represents your level of understanding and comfort with completing that problem on your own.

If any of your bars are less than a 5, choose *one* of those problems and do one of the following tasks:

- Write two questions that you would like to ask about that problem.

- Brainstorm two things that you DO know about that type of problem.

If all of your bars are at 5 or above, choose one problem and do one of these tasks:

- Write two questions you might ask or hints you might give to a student that was stuck on the problem.

- Make a new problem that is similar and more challenging than that problem and solve it.

③ SUPPORTING MY UNDERSTANDING

Now it is time to review your Toolkit for completeness and to revise or update your it to better reflect your current understanding of big ideas.

Refer to the lists provided below and follow your teacher's instructions to revise your Toolkit. This will help make your Toolkit a useful reference.

Learning Log Entries

- Lesson 9.1.4 – Calculating Percents Mentally
- Lesson 9.2.2 – Proportional Relationships
- Lesson 9.2.4 – Methods for Finding Missing Information in Proportional Relationships
- Lesson 9.2.5 – Circumference and Diameter
- Lesson 9.3.1 – Area of a Triangle
- Lesson 9.3.2 - π and the Area of a Circle
- Lesson 9.3.4 – Volume of Prisms and Cylinders

Math Notes

- Lesson 9.1.3 – Division by Fractions
- Lesson 9.1.4 – Calculating Percents by Composition
- Lesson 9.2.4 – Proportional Relationship
- Lesson 9.2.5 – Solving Proportions
- Lesson 9.3.2 – Area of Triangles
- Lesson 9.3.3 – Area of Circles and π
- Lesson 9.3.4 – Prisms, Cylinders, and Their Volumes

Mathematical Vocabulary

The following is a list of vocabulary found in this chapter. The words in bold are the words new to this chapter. Make sure that you are familiar with the terms below. For the words you do not know, refer to the glossary or index. You might also add these words to your Toolkit so that you can reference them in the future.

approximate	base	**circumference**
composition	**cross-products**	**diameter**
discount	equivalent ratios	**exact**
exponent	height	**interest**
multiplier	ordered pair	percent
percent ruler	**pi (π)**	portion
proportional	**radius**	**rate**
ratio	segment	**tax**
tip	whole	

Process Words

calculate	compare	convert
describe	divide	estimate
explain	evaluate	invert
measure	multiply	

Making Connections: Course 1

Answers and Support for Closure Activity #2
Assessing My Understanding

Problem	Solution	Need Help?	More Practice
CL 9-151.	a. 11.4 b. 14.45	Lessons 9.1.1 and 9.1.2 Math Notes box in Lesson 9.1.4 Learning Log (problem 9-39)	Problems 9-6, 9-12, 9-13, 9-14, and 9-40
CL 9-152.	$63.75	Lesson 9.1.3 Math Notes box in Lesson 9.1.4 Learning Log (problem 9-39)	Problems 9-20, 9-21, 9-25, and 9-30
CL9-153.	$9.75	Lesson 9.1.3 Math Notes box in Lesson 9.1.4 Learning Log (problem 9-39)	Problems 9-35 and 9-100
CL 9-154.	Missing values of table are: 6 cans, 10 dollars, 9 cans, 15 dollars, 30 cans, 50 dollars, 27 cans 45 dollars. 	Lessons 9.2.2, 9.2.3 and 9.2.4 Math Notes box in Lesson 9.2.4 Learning Logs (problems 9-63 and 9-82)	Problems 9-57, 9-59, 9-61, 9-71, and 9-81
CL 9-155.	a. $x = 20$ b. $x = \frac{15}{7}$ or $2\frac{1}{7}$ c. $13\frac{1}{3}$ hours or 13 hours 20 minutes	Lessons 9.2.2, 9.2.3 and 9.2.4 Math Notes box in Lesson 9.2.5 Learning Logs (problems 9-63 and 9-82)	Problems 9-81, 9-83, and 9-99

Problem	Solution	Need Help?	More Practice
CL 9-156.	87.96 cm	Lessons 9.2.5 Math Notes box in Lesson 9.2.5 Learning Log (problem 9-96)	Problems 9-102 and 9-115
CL 9-157.	a. 10 square feet b. 153.94 square feet	Lessons 9.3.1 and 9.3.2 Math Notes boxes in Lessons 9.3.1 and 9.3.2 Learning Logs (problem 9-113 and 9-126)	Problems 9-110, 9-111, 9-114, 9-128, 9-125, 9-127, and 9-138
CL 9-158.	a. 133.5 cubic inches b. 2010.62 cubic cm	Lessons 7.1.1, 7.1.2 and 9.3.4 Math Notes box in Lessons 7.2.1 and 9.3.4 Learning Logs (problems 7-19 and 9-145)	Problems 7-3, 7-5, 7-17, 7-20, 9-141, and 9-146

Probability and Survey Design

CHAPTER 10 Probability and Survey Design

In Section 10.1, you will continue your study of probability, extending your learning to include situations involving more than one event. You will learn to identify independent and dependent events and to calculate probabilities of multiple independent events. Finally, you will **compare** theoretical probability to experimental results and determine how this comparison changes as an experiment is conducted many times.

In Section 10.2, you will study the process of taking a survey. You will learn to recognize bias in survey questions and also in the people who are chosen as respondents. You will develop strategies for finding a random and representative sample, so that you can make valid claims about the thoughts of all of the students in your school.

Guiding Questions

Think about these questions throughout this chapter:

How can I represent it?

Is there another way to see it?

Does it make sense?

In this chapter, you will learn how to:

➤ Use experimental results to make and test conjectures about the unknown contents of a bag.

➤ **Compare** experimental and theoretical probabilities.

➤ **Describe** how the relationship between experimental and theoretical probabilities for an experiment changes as the experiment is conducted many times.

➤ Recognize and minimize bias in some survey questions.

➤ Recognize bias in samples chosen to complete surveys.

➤ Attempt to find random and representative samples to complete a survey.

➤ Interpret results of a survey, including analyzing these results for presence of bias.

Chapter Outline

Section 10.1 You will conduct a series of experiments, **comparing** their theoretical and experimental probabilities. In each case you will **compare** these types of probabilities as you conduct the experiment a few times and then as you conduct it many times.

Section 10.2 You will learn to recognize and avoid bias in surveys. You will work with a partner to create a survey question with as little bias as possible. You will also conduct and interpret your own survey.

10.1.1 How can I get the likelihood that I want?

Manipulating the Sample Space

Imagine a game at a carnival where the grand prize is a new car. What would happen if almost everyone who plays wins? To prevent that from happening, people who design games pay close attention to the probability of different possible outcomes of the games.

In this lesson and in the rest of this section, you will consider situations such as the carnival prize as you revisit and extend concepts of probability that you learned in Chapter 5.

10-1. Your team is in charge of the games at the CPM Amusement Park. One of the games involves a robotic arm that grabs a stuffed animal randomly out of a large bin. You need to set up the stuffed animal bin so that the probability of a customer selecting a teddy bear is exactly $\frac{1}{2}$.

a. How would you set up the bin? **Explain**.

b. What if you returned to check on the bin and found that there were four teddy bears left and 12 other animals. What could you add to or remove from the bin to return the probability of selecting a teddy bear to $\frac{1}{2}$?

10-2. Candy Callipso, CEO of the Moon & Mercury Candy Company has hired your team to create bags of colored candies with specific characteristics. Work with your team to decide how many candies of each color you would put in the bag to meet each of the descriptions described below.

a. A bag with 30 candies that are red, blue, and green. The probability of selecting a blue candy should be $\frac{1}{2}$ and the probability of selecting a green candy should be $\frac{1}{3}$.

b. A bag with 100 candies that are blue, green, red, and yellow. The probability of selecting a blue candy should be equal to that of selecting a green candy and twice as much as that of selecting a yellow. The probability of selecting a red candy should be $\frac{1}{5}$.

10-3. Candy Callipso has a crisis! A particular customer ordered a thousand bubblegum machines and specified that they should have a probability of exactly $\frac{1}{3}$ for customers getting a blue gumball. The bubblegum machines were created and sent out, but the customer has called claiming that they were filled incorrectly. Candy's records show that each machine was filled with four yellow gumballs, eight red gumballs, 16 green gumballs, and 20 blue gumballs.

Your task: Work with your team to:

- Figure out whether the machines meet the customer's requirements.

    o If they do, find at least two other combinations of gumballs that would satisfy the picky customer.

    o If they do not, find at least two methods of adjusting the contents of each machine so that the probability of getting a blue gumball is exactly $\frac{1}{3}$.

- Prepare a poster to report to Candy each of your proposed solutions. Be sure to **explain** how you know each solution will work.

Discussion Points

What is the probability to start with?

How can we make the probability greater? How can we make it smaller?

Is there another way?

Further Guidance

10-4. Find the probability of getting each color of gumball in the existing machines.

a. Is the probability of getting a blue gumball too high, too low or just right? How do you know?

b. How could you decrease the probability of getting a blue gumball? Could you add more blue gumballs? Add more gumballs that are not blue? Remove blue gumballs? Remove gumballs that are not blue? **Describe** the effect of each action on the probability of getting a blue gumball.

Problem continues on next page →

Making Connections: Course 1

10-4.   *Problem continued from previous page.*

   c.   In general, how does adding one color affect the probability of getting that color gumball? How would if affect the probability of getting gumballs that are not that color?

   d.   In general, how does subtracting one color affect the probability of getting that color gumball? How would if affect the probability of getting gumballs that are not that color?

10-5.   Jennifer suggested to her team that, since there were 48 gumballs, subtracting four blue gumballs would make the total number of blue gumballs equal to one third of the gumballs. Discuss this with your team. Is Jennifer correct? **Explain** your thinking clearly.

10-6.   David decided that they should just add some of the other colored gumballs so that the blue gumballs are one third of what remains. He suggests that they add six of the green gumballs. Does David's method work? **Explain** clearly how you know that David's method either does or does not work.

10-7.   Work with your team to test different strategies of modifying the gumball dispensers and checking to see if the dispenser meets your boss' criteria. Be sure to keep a record of your work so that you can **explain** your final answer.

10-8.   Make a team poster that shows your team's methods for adjusting the gumball dispensers. Include as a note on your poster indicating which method would waste the fewest gumballs. Be sure to **explain** how your procedure creates dispensers that have a probability for blue gumballs equal to $\frac{1}{3}$.

*Further Guidance
section ends here.*

10-9.   Jessica wants to make a spinner that has all of the following characteristics. Discuss your ideas with your team and sketch a possible spinner for Jessica. Be sure to label the sections of the spinner with a name and their theoretical probability.

   •   Blue, red, purple and green are the only colors on the spinner.

   •   It is half as likely to land on blue as to land on red.

   •   It is three times as likely to land on purple as green.

   •   There is a 50% probability of landing on either blue or red and a 50% probability of landing on either purple or green.

10-10. Tom keeps all his favorite marbles in a special leather bag. Currently the bag contains five red marbles, four blue marbles, and three yellow marbles.

    a. If he randomly chooses one marble to give to a friend, what is the probability that it is blue?

    b. Tom does not really want to give away blue marbles and would like to change the probability that he chooses a blue marble to $\frac{1}{10}$. How many marbles that are not blue could he add to the bag so that the probability of choosing a blue marble becomes $\frac{1}{10}$?

10-11. Imagine that you have a bag containing 10 marbles of different colors. You have drawn a marble, recorded its color, and replaced it fifty times with the following results: nine purple, 16 orange, six yellow, and 19 green marbles. Make a prediction for how many marbles of each color are in the bag. Show all of your work or **explain** your reasoning.

10-12. Find the volume of the following solids.

    a.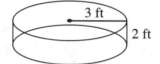

    b.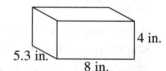

10-13. Molly is reading a mystery titled *Is Polly Gone?*, which is 250 pages long. If she has read 62% of the book, how many pages has she read?

10-4. Convert each fraction to an equivalent decimal rounded to the specified place.

    a. $\frac{3}{8}$ (hundredths)   b. $\frac{1}{6}$ (tenths)

    c. $\frac{4}{3}$ (thousandths)   d. $\frac{4}{13}$ (hundredths)

         Making Connections: Course 1

10.1.2 What if there is more than one event?

Independent and Dependent Events

When you studied probability in Chapter 5, you focused on probabilities of **single events** (for example, one spin of a spinner, one draw of a card, one flip of a coin, or one roll of a number cube). In this chapter, you will begin to investigate outcomes that involve **two or more events**, such as flipping two coins or spinning a spinner twice. Throughout this lesson, use these questions to help focus your team's discussion.

Does the result of one event affect the other?

How many possibilities are there?

10-15. You may remember Chris and her older sister, Rachel, who made a system for determining which one of them washes the dishes each night. Chris has been washing the dishes much more than she feels is her "fair share" so she has come up with a new system. She has proposed to Rachel that they get two coins and each day she and Rachel will take a coin and flip their coins at the same time. If the coins match, Chris washes the dishes and if they do not match, Rachel washes the dishes.

Rachel thinks that this is a good idea and that her little sister is very silly! She thinks to herself, *"Since there are two ways to match the coins, Heads-Heads or Tails-Tails, and only one non-match, a Head and a Tails, then Chris will STILL wash the dishes more often. Ha!"*

a. Do you agree with Rachel? Why or why not?

b. Does it matter if they flip the coins at the same time? That is, does the result of one coin flip depend on the other coin flip?

c. What are all of the possible outcomes when the girls flip their coins? Organize the possibilities into a systematic list.

d. Look at your list from part (c). Imagine that the coins are a penny and a nickel instead of two of the same coin. Does your list include both the possibilities of getting a heads on the penny and tails on the nickel and vice versa? If not, be sure to add them to your list.

e. Is Rachel right? Does this method give her an advantage? What is the theoretical probability for each girl to wash the dishes?

10-16.   ROCK, PAPER, SCISSORS REPRISE

In Chapter 2 you and a partner played the
Rock, Paper, Scissors game. Was this a
fair game? Read the rules (shown again
below) and then discuss this question
with your team.

How to Play

- At the same time as your partner, shake your fist three times and then
  display either a closed fist for "rock," a flat hand for "paper," or a partly
  closed fist with two extended fingers for "scissors."

- Rock beats Scissors (because rock blunts scissors), Scissors beat Paper
  (because scissors cut paper), and Paper beats Rock (because paper can
  wrap up a rock). If you both show the same symbol, repeat the round.

a. While both players are making their choice at the same time, this game has
    two events in every turn. What are the two events?

b. If you and a partner are playing this game and you both "go" at the same
    time, does your choice affect your partner's choice? **Explain**.

c. Are the two events in this game **dependent** (where the outcome of one
    event affects the outcome of the other event) or **independent** (where the
    outcome of one event does *not* affect the outcome of the other event)?
    Explain your reasoning.

d. Work with your team to determine all of the possible outcomes of a game
    of Rock, Paper, Scissors, played by two people (call them Person A and
    Person B). Be sure to include which player wins or if there is a tie for each
    outcome. Be prepared to share your strategies for finding the outcomes
    with the class.

10-17.   Is Rock, Paper, Scissors a fair game? That is, is there an equal likelihood that
          each player will win? How can you tell?

10-18. Imagine that two people, Player A and Player B, were to play the Rock, Paper, Scissors game 12 times.

   a. How many times would you expect Player A to win? Player B to win?

   b. Now, play Rock, Paper, Scissors 12 times with a partner. Record how many times each player wins and how many times the game results in a tie.

   c. How does the experimental probability for the 12 games that you played **compare** to the theoretical probability that each of you will win? Do you expect them to be the same or different? Why?

10-19. Identify the situations below as being either **dependent** or **independent** events.

   a. Flipping a "heads" on a quarter after just flipping a "heads."

   b. Choosing a Jack from a standard deck of cards after choosing a King and not putting it back.

   c. Picking a blue marble from a bag of marbles after picking a blue marble and not putting it back.

   d. Rolling a six on a number cube after getting six, three times in a row.

10-20. LEARNING LOG

   In your Learning Log make an entry that summarizes your understanding of and how to decide if two events are independent or dependent from one another when looking at their likelihood. Give a few examples to support your thinking. Title your entry "Independent and Dependent Events" and include today's date.

10-21.   For each of the following probabilities, write "dependent" if the outcome of the second event depends on the outcome of the first event and "independent" if it does not.

   a.   P(spinning a three on a spinner after having just spun a two)

   b.   P(drawing a red six from a deck of cards after the three of spades was just drawn and not returned to the deck)

   c.   P(drawing a face card from a deck of cards after a jack was just drawn and replaced and the deck shuffled again)

   d.   P(selecting a lemon-lime soda if the person before you reaches into a cooler full of lemon-lime sodas, removes one, and drinks it)

10-22.   Lalo has a circular trampoline with a diameter of eight meters.

   a.   What is the circumference of the trampoline?

   b.   What is the area of the trampoline?

10-23.   Ms. Baumgartner can travel 480 miles in 8 hours. At this rate, how many hours would it take her to complete an 810-mile trip? Show how you know.

10-24.   Find the value of the variable that makes each equation true.

   a. $4k + 1 = -7$ b. $30 - 5x = 10$

10-25.   Simlify each of the following expressions.

   a. $\frac{11}{12} + \frac{4}{9}$ b. $4\frac{3}{5} - 1\frac{13}{15}$ c. $\frac{9}{10} \cdot 2\frac{1}{3}$ d. $12 \div \frac{7}{8}$

10.1.3   How can I find all of the outcomes?

Probability Tables

As you may have noticed in the previous lesson, considering probabilities when there is more than one event *and* there are more than two possibilities for each event (such as with the Rock, Paper Scissors game), keeping track of all outcomes can be a challenge. In this lesson, you will learn about **probability tables**, a new strategy for organizing all of the possibilities in a game such as this.

10-26.   TEN O's

In this game, you will create a strategy to play a board game based on your predictions of likely outcomes. Your teacher will roll two number cubes and add the resulting numbers. As your teacher rolls the number cubes and calls out each sum, you will cross out an O over the number called. The goal of the game is to be the first person to cross out all ten of your O's.

Talk with your team about the possible outcomes of this game and then draw a number line like the one below on your own paper. Place a total of ten O's on your number line. Each O should be placed above a number, and you should distribute them based on what results you think your teacher will get.

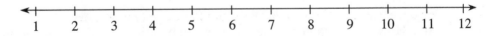

Follow your teacher's instructions to play the game.

10-27. Gerald's strategy for the Ten O's game was to place an O on each number from 1 to 10. He was frustrated that his strategy of placing his ten O's was not working, so he decided to analyze the game.

Gerald began by creating the table at right to list all of the possible combinations of rolls.

a. Did he list them all? If so, how can you be sure that they are all there? If not, give examples of a few that he has missed.

b. Does Gerald's table include information about the sums for each possible roll of the two number cubes? What could be added to help analyze this game more easily?

Cube 1	Cube 2
1	1
2	2
3	3
4	4
5	5
6	6
1	2
2	3
3	4
4	5
5	6
1	3
2	4
3	5
4	6
1	4
2	5
3	6
1	5
2	6
1	6

10-28. Gerald decided that this method was taking too long and was too confusing. Even if he listed all of the combinations, he still had to find the sums and then find the theoretical probabilities for each one. Inspired by multiplication tables, he decided to try to **make sense** of the problem by organizing the possibilities in a table like the one shown at right.

+	1	2	3	4	5	6
1	2	3				
2	3	4				
3	4					
4						
5						
6						

a. How does Gerald's table represent the two events in this situation? What should go in each of the empty cells? Discuss this with your team and then complete Gerald's table on your own paper.

b. How many total possible number combinations are there for rolling the two cubes? Is each combination equally likely? That is, is the probability of getting two 1's the same as that of getting two 2's or a 3 and a 1?

c. How many ways are there to get each sum? Are there any numbers on the game board that are not possible to achieve?

d. What is the theoretical probability for getting each sum listed on the Ten O's game board?

e. Now work with your team to determine a better strategy for Gerald to place his ten O's on the game board that you think will help him to win this game. **Explain** your strategy and your reasoning.

10-29.   Gloria and Jenny each have only one O left on their game board. Gloria's O is at 6 and Jenny's is at 8. Which student is more likely to win on the next roll? **Explain**.

10-30.   Now go back and analyze the game of Rock, Paper, Scissors using a probability table to determine the possible outcomes.

    a.   Make a probability table and use it to find the probabilities of Player A winning and of Player B winning. Did you get the same answers as before?

    b.   Do the probabilities for Player A winning and Player B winning add up to 1 (or 100%)? If not, why not?

10-31.   Imagine that you have a bag with a red block, a blue block , a green block, and a yellow block inside. You plan to make two draws from the bag, replacing the block in between each draw.

    a.   Are these two events (the drawing of a block) independent or dependent? Does it matter if you replace the block each time? Why or why not?

    b.   Find the probability of getting a red block and a blue block. (Either color can come first.) Be ready to share your method of organizing the possible outcomes.

ETHODS AND MEANINGS

Independent and Dependent Events

MATH NOTES

Two events are **independent** if the outcome of one event does not affect the outcome of the other event. For example, if you draw a card from a deck but replace it before you draw again, the outcomes of the two draws are independent.

Two events are **dependent** if the outcome of one event affects the outcome of the other event. For example, if you draw a card from a deck and do not replace it for the next draw, the outcomes of the two draws are dependent.

10-32.   Find the area of each shaded portion below, if the entire square represents one whole. Can you find the answer in more than one way?

a.

b.

10-33.   Magali was at the State Fair and decided to buy a sundae from an ice cream stand. The ice cream stand had four flavors of ice cream (chocolate, vanilla, mint chip, and avocado coconut) and two toppings (hot fudge and caramel). How many different sundaes could Magali create using one scoop of ice cream and one topping? Use a diagram or make a list to support your answer.

10-34.   Simplify each of the following expression without using a calculator.

a. $-7 + 3(-4) + 5(2 + 9)$

b. $3.04 + 0.8 - 0.61$

c. $(-2.4)(-0.01)$

d. $\frac{1}{3} \cdot 12 + \frac{5}{6}$

10-35.   Find the perimeter and area of each of the triangles below.

a.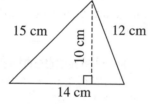

15 cm   10 cm   12 cm

14 cm

b.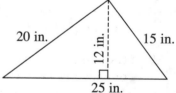

20 in.   12 in.   15 in.

25 in.

10-36.   **Multiple Choice:** A shirt that normally costs $35 is on sale for 25% off the original price. What is the sale price? Show how you know.

A. $26.25   B. $8.75   C. $43.75   D. $28.75

10-37.   Solve each of the following proportions.

a. $\frac{3 \text{ minutes}}{60 \text{ words}} = \frac{x}{360 \text{ words}}$

b. $\frac{5 \text{ sodas}}{\$1.30} = \frac{8 \text{ sodas}}{C}$

c. $\frac{4 \text{ days}}{5 \text{ pizzas}} = \frac{x}{35 \text{ pizzas}}$

d.   Write a word problem that could be solved by one of the proportions in parts (a) through (c).

Making Connections: Course 1

10.1.4 How can I find it more efficiently?

Using Multiplication to Calculate Probabilities

What if you were working with an entire deck of cards and you wanted to find the probability of drawing the Ace of Spades two times in a row? Would it **make sense** to make a list of all possible outcomes? What about to make a probability table?

Today you will learn a strategy for calculating probabilities for **compound** (more than one) **independent events** that will allow you to consider situations such as this one with many possible outcomes efficiently.

10-38.   Imagine spinning the spinner at right two times.

   a.   What would be the probability of spinning a red on your first spin? Write this as a fraction. What would be the probability of spinning a red on your second spin (also as a fraction)? Are the outcomes of these two spins dependent or independent? **Explain**.

   b.   Work with your team to make a probability table to represent this situation. What is the probability for spinning each color on the first spin? The second spin? How can you see these fractions in your table?

   c.   What is the probability for spinning a red on the first spin and then spinning a red on the second spin? Work with your team to find **at least two ways** to find this.

   d.   How are the probabilities of two individual events and the probability of the combined events related? For example, how could you find the probability of spinning a blue and then a yellow without using a table?

10-39.   Consider the spinner at right.

   a.   How is the probability for spinning each color on this spinner different from the spinner in problem 10-38? Find the probability for spinning each color for this spinner.

   b.   If this spinner is spun two times, will the results of the two spins be independent of each other? **Explain**.

Problem continues on next page →

10-39.   *Problem continued from previous page.*

    c.   Make a probability table to represent spinning this spinner twice. How is your probability table for this situation similar to and how is it different from the one in problem 10-38.

    d.   For this spinner, what is the probability of spinning a red and then another red? Work with your team to find this probability in **at least two ways**. That is, show how this probability can be found in the probability table and how it can be found without the use of the table.

10-40.   At the school fair, students play a game called Flip and Spin in which a player first flips a coin and then spins the spinner shown at right. If the coin comes up heads and the spinner lands on red, the player wins a stuffed animal. If the coin comes up tails and the spinner lands on yellow, the player gets another turn to play. If the spinner lands on green, the player's turn is over (whether the coin comes up heads or on tails).

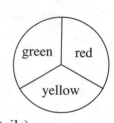

    a.   Calculate the probability that you will win a stuffed animal on the first play. Also find the probability of getting another turn and of losing your turn. Use **more than one method** to show your thinking. Be prepared to share your strategies with the class.

    b.   How would the outcomes change if someone were to spin first and then flip the coin? How would the outcomes change if someone were to spin and another person were to flip a coin at the same time? **Explain**.

10-41.   Find the probability of each of the outcomes of compound events described below.

    a.   Flipping a coin and getting "heads" and picking a Jack from a standard deck of cards.

    b.   Rolling a five on a number cube and then rolling a six.

    c.   Flipping a coin and getting "tails" and then choosing the one blue marble in a bag of 12 marbles.

    d.   Picking the Ace of spades from a standard deck of cards, putting it back, mixing them up and picking the Ace of spades again.

Making Connections: Course 1

10-42.   LEARNING LOG

In your Learning Log, show all of the methods you know to
find probabilities for multiple events. Title your entry
"Finding Probabilities of Compound Events" and label it
with today's date.

10-43.   A coin is tossed and a card is drawn from a standard deck of cards. What is the
probability of getting each of the following results:

a.   A head and a spade?

b.   A tail and a King?

c.   A head and the Jack of diamonds?

10-44.   For Shelley's birthday on Saturday, she received two new shirts (one plaid and
one striped), three pairs of shorts (tan, yellow, and green), and two pairs of
shoes (sandals and tennis shoes). On Monday she wants to wear a completely
new outfit. How many possible outfit choices does she have from these new
clothes? Show a diagram or **explain** your reasoning.

10-45.   Ed wants to buy a new chair. He found one that he really likes and it is marked
down 25% from the original price of $140.

a.   How much less money will he have to pay than if he bought the chair at its
original price?

b.   What is the sale price of Ed's chair?

c.   Find 75% of $140.

d.   **Explain** why the answers for parts (b) and (c) are the same.

10-46.   Without a calculator, add $1 + \frac{1}{2} + \frac{1}{3} + \frac{1}{4}$ and write your answer
as a mixed number.

10-47.   **Multiple Choice:** Which quotient *does not* equal 1? **Explain** or show how you
know.

A. $3\frac{4}{5} \div \frac{19}{5}$ B. $\frac{1}{8} \div 0.125$ C. $1\frac{2}{3} \div \frac{3}{5}$ D. $\frac{5}{6} \div \frac{5}{6}$

10.1.5   What can I predict?

Comparing Theoretical and Experimental Probabilities

In this lesson you will calculate probabilities of compound events and you will return to the Color-Rama game, analyzing all of the colors a player could choose. You will also conduct an experiment, **comparing** results you can predict mathematically with what actually happens. You will think about how this comparison changes as an experiment is conducted many times.

As you work with your team today, keep these questions in mind:

How can we count all of the possible outcomes?

What results do we expect?

How do our results **compare** with our predictions?

10-48.   CRAZY COINS, part 1

Imagine tossing three coins.

a.   How many events would this be? Are the events independent or dependent?

b.   As you discovered in Lesson 10.1.4, one way to find the theoretical probability for two events happening is to find the product of the probabilities of those two events.

Do you think that this method will work if there are more than two events? For example, would this work to find the probability of getting three heads? Work with your team to check this. In other words, calculate the probability by multiplying and by some other method. Be prepared to **explain** your conclusions to the class.

c.   What is the probability of flipping two heads and a tail? What about three tails? Why are these answers different?

Making Connections: Course 1

10-49.   ANALYZING COLOR-RAMA

Now you will analyze the Color-Rama Game to determine why each color does not have the same probability of winning. The rules for Color-Rama as well as a diagram of the game board are provided below for your reference.

Yellow   Green   Purple   Orange   Purple   Green   Yellow

Game Rules

1. Each player chooses one of the colors on the Color-Rama Game board. No two players may choose the same color.

2. Place a marker on the orange square.

3. The players take turn flipping the +/– coin three times to determine how to move the marker. Each time, a + comes up, the marker moves one square to the right. Each time a – comes up, the marker moves one square to the left.

4. If the marker lands on your color, you win.

---

a.   With your team, consider the connection between this game and tossing three coins in the previous problem. How many outcomes are possible for this game? **Explain**.

b.   Connect outcomes of the coin flips to the resulting colors in Color-Rama and show the theoretical probability of the marker landing on each color after three coin flips. Which color would you choose next time you play?

10-50.   CRAZY COINS, part 2

Work with your team on parts (a) through (f) below, as you return to the case of three coins, considering theoretical probabilities and **comparing** them to experimental results.

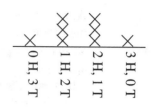

a.   Calculate the probability of getting 0, 1, 2, or 3 tails when you flip three coins.

b.   If you were to flip three coins 16 times, how many times would you expect to get 0, 1, 2, or 3 tails?

c.   Obtain three coins from your teacher and flip them 16 times. Write down how many times you get 0, 1, 2, or 3 tails. How do these results **compare** with the predictions that you made?

d.   Combine your results with those of the rest of the class. Write down the experimental probabilities for getting 0, 1, 2, or 3 tails, based on your class's results. How do these results **compare** with the theoretical probabilities?

e.   Follow your teacher's instructions to use a technology tool to flip three coins 1000 times and then write the new experimental probability. Again, how do these results **compare** with the theoretical probabilities?

f.   Work with your team to write a statement about how the relationship between theoretical and experimental probabilities changes as an experiment is conducted many times. Be prepared to share your statement with the class.

10-51.   SILLY SPINNERS

At the school carnival, Raquel was
watching a game involving the spinners
shown at right. In the game, each player
spins one of the spinners. The player
whose spinner lands on a higher number
wins the game. Raquel wants to play the
game and wonders which spinner she
should choose or if it even matters.

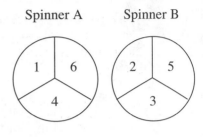

Spinner A   Spinner B

a.   Work with your team to help Raquel decide which, if either, spinner is most
      likely to win by finding all of the possible outcomes and the theoretical
      probabilities for each spinner to be the winning one.

b.   Raquel wants to create a fair game with spinners that she can play with her
      sister. Her sister thinks that if she uses two spinners, she should come out
      with a fair game because two is an even number. Do you agree? Why or
      why not.

c.   Is it possible for Rachel to make a fair game using two spinners with three
      equal areas like the ones above? If it is possible, then show two spinners
      that would work. If it is not possible, then **explain** why not.

10-52.   LEARNING LOG

In your Learning Log, write down what you have learned
about calculating probabilities of multiple independent
events. Be sure to include examples to demonstrate your
thinking. Title this entry, "Calculating Compound
Probabilities" and label it with today's date.

10-53.   Before you leave class today, obtain a Lesson 10.1.5A or 10.1.5B Resource
          Page, take the survey, and hand it to your teacher. The results will be important
          for Lesson 10.2.1.

METHODS AND MEANINGS

Calculating Probabilities of Independent Events

When you know the probability of each of two separate events, the probability of them both occurring is called the **compound probability**.

To find the **compound probability of independent events**, you can find the probability of each event separately and then multiply the probabilities. Using the example of rolling a one followed by a six on a number cube:

$$P(1) = \tfrac{1}{6} \text{ and } P(6) = \tfrac{1}{6} \text{ so } P(1 \text{ and } 6) = \tfrac{1}{6} \cdot \tfrac{1}{6} = \tfrac{1}{36}$$

Finding the compound probability of dependent events is more complicated and will be developed in future courses.

10-54.   Larry and Barry are playing a game using a penny and a number cube. Larry gets a point for every "three" that is rolled. Barry gets a point for every "head" that is flipped. Is this game fair? Why or why not?

10-55.   The spinner at right is spun twice. Calculate the probability of each of the following outcomes.

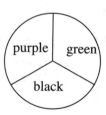

a.   Getting black twice?

b.   Getting green twice?

Making Connections: Course 1

10-56.   Kelso's Mom wants to put a floating blanket over his circular wading pool to keep the heat in and the leaves out. The pool has a diameter of 10 feet.

   a.   How many square feet of blanket will be part of the blanket?

   b.   If the pool supply store charges $0.10 per square foot for the blanket, how much will the material for the blanket cost?

10-57.   Ryan and Janelle are each driving from a different location to meet at Mammoth Lakes. When they each stopped for lunch they called each other on their cell phones. Ryan had traveled 245 miles in $3\frac{1}{2}$ hours. Janelle had driven 260 miles in 4 hours.

   a.   How fast was each person driving?

   b.   If Janelle originally started 575 miles from Mammoth Lakes and continues traveling at the same rate (from part (a)), how many more hours will it take her to arrive at her destination?

10-58.   **Multiple Choice:** Which of the following fractions is closest to 1? **Explain** how you can tell.

   A. $\frac{5}{8}$ B. $\frac{19}{20}$ C. $1\frac{1}{5}$ D. $1\frac{3}{20}$

10.2.1 Is the question biased?

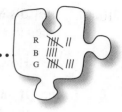

Detecting Bias in Survey Questions

Have you ever heard statements such as these:

- "81% of public school students are not satisfied with the food provided by their schools."

- "The President has an approval rating of 72%."

How do news sources find out this information? Do they ask every public school student? Do they ask every citizen? And what questions do they ask?

Generally, to make claims such as these, someone has taken a survey. In this section, you will study surveys, examining how likely the survey is to generate correct results. You will start by examining how survey questions are asked and how they may bias results.

As you think about survey questions, consider the following questions.

Is the question phrased in a way
that will let me present the data easily?

Does the question influence the way
people are likely to answer?

Is the question fair for everyone?

Can I influence the outcome by
changing the way I ask the question?

10-59.   Obtain a Lesson 10.2.1A Resource Page and data from the polls that were taken at the end of Lesson 10.1.5.

a. Calculate the portion of survey takers who responded in the given ways on Survey A and Survey B. Express each portion as a fraction and a percent.

b. Were there any questions for which the responses were more difficult to quantify than others? How could these questions have been rewritten to make the responses clearer?

510

10-60.   When an answer is influenced by the way a question is asked, the question is said to contain **bias**. The questions posed to your classmates in Polls A and B are reprinted below. There are descriptions in parts (a) through (f) below of some techniques survey takers often use to influence results.

Work with your team to decide which, if any, of the survey questions presented to your class use each of the techniques.

	Poll A	Poll B
1.	Do teenagers worry about their grades?	Do teenagers worry about getting poor grades?
2.	Do you support the Governor's education plan that ensures that students will be more successful in school?	Do you support the Governor's education plan?
3.	Does violence in movies and video games affect young people?	Does the frequent occurrence of brutal violence in movies and video games have a negative affect on the young people exposed to them?
4.	Do you believe the current movie ratings system (G, PG, PG-13, R) is effective?	Do you believe the current movie ratings system (G, PG, PG-13, R) is effective?
5.	Should school districts spend more money on higher teacher salaries?	Should your math teacher be paid more?
6.	Moderate exercise is necessary to stay beautiful and healthy. Do you exercise regularly?	Do you exercise regularly?

a. **Question Order:** Sometimes two questions are asked in an order such that the first question suggests an answer to the second. Which of the poll questions uses the "question order" technique? Why would you expect it to influence responses?

b. **Preface:** Some questions start with statements that can bias the result of the question that follows. Which of the survey questions presented to your class uses this technique? Why would you expect such statements to influence responses?

c. **Two Questions in One:** This technique involves asking two questions at once. Survey takers may agree with one part and disagree with another part, but they are only allowed to give one answer. Which of the survey questions presented to your class uses this technique?

Problem continues on next page →

10-60.   *Problem continued from previous page.*

    d. **Biased Wording:** By using adjectives, pleasing or unpleasant words, the surveyor can influence results. Which of the survey questions presented to your class uses this technique?

    e. **Desire To Please:** Research shows that many survey takers will answer in the ways that they perceive will please the surveyor. Which of the survey questions presented to your class are likely to be biased in this way? Are some more severely biased than others?

10-61.   With your team, consider each of the survey questions below. Decide if any bias techniques are being used to influence the survey results. If no bias technique is being used, write, "Fair question." Be prepared to **explain** your thinking to the class.

    a. Jolly Juice has twice the Vitamin E of other brands. Which brand of juice is the healthiest?

    b. Do you think that people who hurt defenseless animals should be punished?

    c. Do you agree that Hal Poppington is the best man to be elected Mayor?

    d. What is your favorite kind of juice?

10-62.   You and your team members work for the U.S. Department of Education. You have been asked to survey people about the President's new proposal to extend the school year from the current 180 days to 200 days. A survey question might be, "Do you think students should attend school for 180 days as they do now, or for 200 days?"

    Use the technique assigned by your teacher to rewrite the question to bias responses to be more favorable to the 200-day school year.

Making Connections: Course 1

10-63.   Survey questions can be either **open** or **closed**. Open questions allow free response, while closed questions have a limited number of possible responses. Open questions allow survey takers to express their ideas or opinions most accurately, but responses are generally difficult for surveyors to organize and analyze. Closed questions allow only a limited number of responses, which the researcher knows before doing the survey; the advantage is that the resulting data is often easier to quantify and graph.

Classify the following questions as either "open" or "closed."

a.   How often do you exercise?

   A.   Every day   B.   Once a week or more   C.   Less than once a week

b.   What is your favorite way to exercise?

c.   What is your favorite time of year?

d.   In which country were you born?

10-64.   For each question in problem 10-63 that you decided is open, give examples of answers that might be difficult to **compare** and quantify. For each question that you decided is closed, **explain** how the information you get from an answer may not be as accurate as it could be.

10-65.   Through the next few class periods, you will work with a partner to participate in a survey project. Your teacher will assign you and your partner a survey question to work with. Work with your partner to analyze your question by answering the questions in parts (a) through (e) below.

a.   Is your survey question open or closed?

b.   It is possible for you to get too many different answers to your questions to analyze your results well? If so, how could you reword your question so that your answers could be grouped and analyzed? Work with your partner to rewrite or change your question, if necessary. Ask your teacher to approve your new question.

10-66. Consider each of the following survey questions. For each one, **explain** any bias you can find. If you think the question is unbiased (or fair), **explain** why.

    a. Do you agree that it is important to make ending homelessness a high priority?

    b. Which of the following factors is most important to address in order to slow global climate change?

        A. Car emissions   B. Airplane emissions

        C. Pollutants from private industry   D. Dependence on oil

    c. How important is it that teacher salaries be raised?

10-67. Steve and Cathy are playing a card game with a standard deck of 52 playing cards. Cathy is dealt an ace and a four. Steve is dealt a jack.

    a. How many cards are left in the deck?

    b. How many of the remaining cards are aces?

    c. If Steve gets an ace, he will win. What is the probability that he will get an ace on the next card he is dealt?

    d. Next Steve gets a two and Cathy gets a five. Now Steve wants a nine. What is the probability that he will get a nine on the next card he is dealt?

10-68. Find the lettered angles in the figures below.

    a.
$137°$
m k

    b.
$27°$
$129°$ W

10-69. Multiple Choice: What is the least common multiple of 12 and 9?

   A. 3   B.   108   C.   72   D.   36

10-70. Multiple Choice: What is the greatest common factor of 24 and 36?

   A. 72   B.   6   C.   12   D.   18

10-71. Solve each of the following problems, showing all of your work.

   a. Ten friends are going to share $3\frac{1}{3}$ pounds of ice cream. How large is each person's share?

   b. Ten yards of ribbon is cut into pieces that are each $3\frac{1}{3}$ yards long. How many pieces are there?

10.2.2 Is the survey fair?

Representative Samples

If you want to know what a dish of food tastes like, do you need to eat all of the food in the dish? Or can you get a good idea of the taste by trying a small amount?

When conducting a survey, it is not usually possible to survey every person in the **population** of interest (residents of the United States, students at your school, etc.). Instead, statisticians collect information about a **sample** (a portion) of the population. However, finding a sample that represents the whole population well (a **representative sample**) is not easy.

As you work with your team today, keep these questions in mind:

> Do all of the survey takers have
> similar characteristics?
>
> How can we find survey takers to represent
> the major characteristics of the population?
>
> How well can we expect this sample
> to represent the larger population?

10-72.   When you analyze results from your own survey, you will want to make claims about the thoughts or opinions of *all* of the students in your school. If you were to survey only students in the cooking club, for example, it might be hard to make claims about what all students think. Consider this idea as you think about the **samples** described below.

a.   If you wanted to generalize the opinions of all students at your school, would it **make sense** to go to a bank and survey the people there? Why or why not?

b.   If you wanted to generalize the opinions of all students at your school, would it **make sense** to ask all of your friends at school? Why or why not?

c.   If you wanted to generalize the opinions of all students at your school, would it **make sense** to ask every third person at the school bus stop? Why or why not?

Making Connections: Course 1

10-73. There are a variety of ways to choose samples of the population you are studying. Every sample has features that make it more or less representative of the larger population. For example, if you want to represent all of the students at your school, but you survey all of the students at school 30 minutes after the last class has ended, you are likely to get a disproportionate number of students who play sports or who attend after school activities or who do not work.

   a. If you ask the opinion of the people around you, then you have conducted a **convenience sample**. If you took a convenience sample right now, what would be some features of the sample? Would you expect a convenience sample to represent the entire student population at your school? Why or why not?

   b. If you mail a questionnaire and accept all the returned responses, then you have taken a **written survey**. What are some features of the sample used for a written survey? Could it represent well the sample of all of the students at school?

   c. If you devise a system so that each person in the population has an equal chance of being surveyed, then you have a **random sample**. What is a feature of a random sample? What drawbacks might come with using a random sample?

10-74. From what population is each of these samples taken? Write down the actual population for each of these sampling techniques.

Method of Sampling	Description of Actual Population
Call every hundredth name in the phone book.	People with phones who have their numbers listed
Call people at home at 10 a.m.	
Ask every tenth person who leaves the mall.	
Ask people leaving the bank.	
Mail questionnaires to people.	
Ask everyone on the school bus.	

10-75.   In 1988, the steering Committee of the Physicians Health Study Research Group released the results of a five-year experiment conducted on over 22,000 male physicians aged 40 to 84. The research on this sample suggested that the participants who took an aspirin every other day had a lower rate of heart attacks.

    a.   Can you legitimately conclude from this study that aspirin reduces the risk of heart attacks for all people? Why or why not?

    b.   Can you legitimately conclude from this study that aspirin reduces heart attacks for all men? Why or why not?

    c.   Can you legitimately conclude from this study that aspirin reduces heart attacks for all men aged 40 to 84? Why or why not?

    d.   Can you legitimately conclude from this study that aspirin reduces heart attacks for male physicians aged 40 to 84? Why or why not?

    e.   Can you legitimately conclude from this study that male physicians aged 40 to 84 should take aspirin? Why or why not?

10-76.   To determine whether a sample is representative of a larger population, it is useful to keep track of some **characteristics** (features or qualities) of the sample. For example, a few characteristics of the sample of people you might find waiting for the bus alone early in the morning are that they take the bus, they have jobs or go to school, and they are adolescents or adults.

    Work with your partner to decide on four characteristics of your respondents you will monitor in order to determine how representative your sample is. Be prepared to share your ideas with the class.

10-77.   Set up a table like the one below to organize the information you gather in your survey. Leave room to organize responses from 50 respondents.

Put your survey question here.

#	Name	Char 1	Char 2	Char 3	Char 4	Response
1						
2						
3						

10-78.   Suppose you were conducting a survey to try to determine what portion of voters in your town support a particular candidate for mayor. Consider each of the following methods for sampling the voting population of your town. State whether each is likely to produce a representative sample and **explain** your reasoning.

a.   Call one number from each page of the phone book between noon and 2 p.m.

b.   Survey each person leaving a local grocery store.

c.   Survey each person leaving a local movie theater.

d.   Walk around downtown and survey every fourth person you see.

e.   Could you make a representative sample by surveying a few people from each of the situations described in parts (a) through (d) above? **Explain**.

10-79.   For the following experiments, write "dependent" if the second event depends on the outcome of the first and "independent" if the first event does not affect the outcome of the second event.

   a.   Flipping a coin and getting tails after you have already flipped it once and gotten tails.

   b.   Drawing a king from a deck of cards after a card was taken out and not returned to the deck.

   c.   Drawing an ace from a deck of cards after a card was drawn, replaced, and the deck shuffled again.

   d.   Getting a peppermint candy from a jar of mixed candies after you just took out and ate a lemon candy.

   e.   Choose one of the situations described in parts (a) through (d) and **explain** why you chose either independent or dependent.

10-80.   Calculate each of the following percentages. Show all of your work or **explain** your reasoning.

   a.   20% of 340   b.   15% of 130   c.   15% of 105   d.   18% of 137

10-81.   Copy and complete the table at right with values of x and y that work for the rule $xy = 100$.

x	y
5	
10	
−1	
	2.5
$\frac{1}{4}$	
	−25
200	

10.2.3 How can I conduct a fair survey?

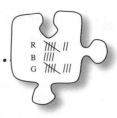

Conducting a Survey and Interpreting Results

Now you will learn to minimize the amount of bias in a survey and to make sure it is not influenced greatly by outside factors. You will also examine strategies for displaying and communicating survey results, and you will apply this knowledge to the survey you are taking.

10-82. A good surveyor tries to keep the people being surveyed from being biased by outside experiences. Imagine that you and your team will be conducting a taste test to **compare** Jolly Grape Juice and Great Grape Juice.

a. How can you make sure that people will not be influenced by what they already think about their favorite juice?

b. If four people all taste the two juices at the same time, how can you make sure they do not influence each other's opinions by talking about their impressions?

c. Could the temperature of the juices make a difference? How would you reduce any influence that temperature could have?

10-83. Talk with your partner about how the kinds of bias described in problem 10-56 may have affected the responses to your survey. Be prepared to share your ideas with the class.

10-84. Throughout this course, you have studied a number of ways to organize data visually.

a. Make a list of all the different ways you know to display data.

b. Which of the graphs you listed in part (a) will you use to present your data from the survey question you were assigned?

10-85.   Work with your partner to complete your survey project and prepare your presentation. In order for your project to be complete, you need to do each of the following tasks.

a.   Finish surveying students and prepare your tally sheet.

b.   Create a graphical display of student responses. Note that you may need to categorize your data. Your graph should be clear and easy to read from a distance.

c.   Prepare responses to these questions.

   i.   Calculate the percent of your sample that gave each of the possible responses. For example, you might calculate that 27% of the people in your sample prefer winter to all other seasons.

   ii.   How did you attempt to find a random, representative sample of the population? For example, did you make sure to survey an equal number of boys and girls?

   iii.   Calculate the percent of your sample with each of the four characteristics you monitored. For each of them, how do they **compare** to the percentages of the entire student population with each of these characteristics? For example, you might say that 54% of the sample is made up of students who you know, and you know approximately 20% of the students at the school.

   iv.   What are some possible sources of bias to think about when looking at the results of your own survey?

10-86. Some data, such as that from your survey, counts different values of *one* variable. For example, your survey might count how many people choose blue as their favorite color.

Other data **compares** values of *two* variables. For example, the scatter plot at right shows the number of pages in books **compared** to the prices of those books.

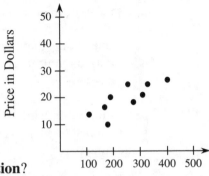

Number of Pages

a. How many books are represented in this scatter plot?

b. Does the graph show a **positive correlation**? (As one variable increases in value, does the other variable increase as well?)

c. What does this graph tell you about the relationship between the number of pages in the book and its price?

d. Does an increase in the number of pages cause an increase in the price?

10-87. What would it mean for data to show a **negative correlation**? What might it look like in a graph? Discuss this with your team and be prepared to share your ideas with the class.

10-88. After the algebra final exam, Octavio surveyed eleven students about how much time they spent studying. Octavio's data is shown in the table at right.

a. Does this data show a positive correlation? (As one value increases, does the other value also increase?)

b. Gus claims that the more time you spend studying, the higher your test scores will be. Is his opinion supported by the data? **Explain**.

Hours spent studying	Test Scores (Percent)
10	90
$5\frac{1}{2}$	70
12	97
7	85
6	80
$2\frac{2}{3}$	55
15	100
1	20
10	85
4	70
8	85

10-89.   After the next algebra test, Lena gave the same
         survey as Octavio to 3 different people. Her data
         is shown in the table at right.

hours spent studying	test scores (%)
7	65
2	80
3	75

   a.   Does this data show a positive correlation?

   b.   Lena claims that her data shows that if you study too much, you will do
        badly on your tests. Who do you believe, Lena, Gus, or neither? Why?

10-90.   In the double-line graph below, the darker line represents sales of hot chocolate
         from August to July, while the lighter line represents the sales of tissue in the
         same time period.

   a.   Do the sales of tissues and hot chocolate appear to be correlated or
        somehow connected?

   b.   Does the sale of tissue *cause* the increase in the sale of hot chocolate?
        Explain.

   c.   Why could it **make sense** that the data seem to be related as represented
        by the line graph?

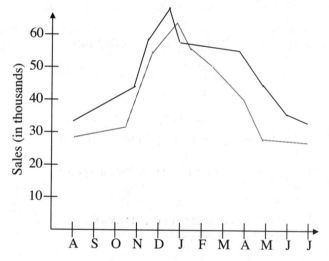

10-91. Do the following **causal relationships** claimed **make sense**? In other words, is it possible that the first event described could cause the second? **Explain** your answer in a complete sentence.

    a. An increase in the number of pages in a book could cause an increase in the cost of the book.

    b. An increase in shoe size could cause an increase in spelling ability.

    c. An increase in the number of years of education could cause an increase in salary.

    d. An increase in facial tissue sales could cause an increase in hot chocolate sales.

    e. An increase in walking time could cause an increase in weight loss.

    f. An increase in a husband's age could cause an increase in the wife's age.

10-92. Graph the following data as a scatter plot.

    a. Does the graph show either a positive or a negative correlation?

    b. Does there appear to be a connection between height and spelling ability?

    c. Does greater height cause better spelling ability?

    d. What other factors could create the correlation you see?

Height (Inches)	Test Scores (Percent)
24	3
56	86
72	98
49	50
18	0
36	12
70	90
66	81
61	75
34	25
59	80
57	77
64	88

10-93. Multiple Choice: Which of the following fractions is closest to 1? **Explain** how you can tell.

    A. $\frac{19}{18}$ B. $\frac{19}{20}$ C. $1\frac{1}{15}$ D. $\frac{17}{18}$

10-94.   Ann and Nate's math class had a popcorn party. Each student made a container for popcorn by rolling up a piece of paper that was 11 inches long by 14 inches wide. Ann made a narrow tube by using the 14-inch side for the height. Nate made his tube shorter and wider by using the 10-inch side for the height.

Whose tube holds the most popcorn? How much more does it hold than the other tube?

10-95.   Linnea and Teagan went shopping. Linnea bought a $70 coat at 30% off and an $80 pair of shoes at 40% off. Teagan bought a $70 pair of shoes at 40% off and an $80 coat at 30% off. Who spent more? How much more?

10-96.   When Isaac went out to dinner, his bill was $72. He is trying to decide how much money to leave for a tip. Help him by calculating each of the following percentages. Show all of your work.

   a.   20%   b.   15%   c.   18%

10-97.   On a coordinate grid, plot the points (2, 3), (4, 6), and (7, 3).

   a.   Connect the points to form a triangle.

   b.   Find the area of this triangle.

10-98.   Estimate the value of each of the following expressions and **explain** your reasoning. Then check your estimations by calculating them.

   a. $2\frac{3}{5} + 1\frac{3}{4}$ b. $1\frac{4}{9} - \frac{1}{2}$ c. $\frac{5}{8} \cdot \frac{7}{12}$ d. $\frac{4}{7} \div 1\frac{3}{5}$

10-99.   The shape at right is composed of a rectangle and a semi-circle (half of a circle).

   a.   Find the perimeter.

   b.   Find the area.

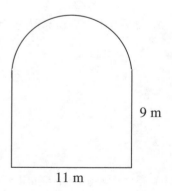

9 m

11 m

Glossary

5-D process   An organized method to solve problems. The 5 D's stand for Describe/Draw, Define, Do, Decide, and Declare. This is a problem-solving strategy for which solving begins by making a prediction, and then confirming whether or not the result is correct. If not, information is gained about how close the trial is to the correct value, so that adjustments may be made. Being organized is extremely important to the success of this method, as well as writing a usable table. The 5-D process leads to writing equations to represent word problems.

absolute value   The absolute value of a number is the distance of the number from zero. Since the absolute value represents a distance, without regard to direction, absolute value is always non-negative. Thus, the absolute value of a negative number is its opposite, while the absolute value of a non-negative number is just the number itself. The absolute value of x is usually written "$|x|$." For example, $|-5| = 5$ and $|22| = 22$.

acute angle   An angle with a measure greater than 0° and less than 90°. An example is shown at right.

acute triangle   A triangle with all three angle measures less than 90°.

addition $(+)$ An operation that tells how many objects there are when two sets are combined. The result is the number of objects in the two sets together which is called a sum. In arithmetic, the word "object" usually means "number."

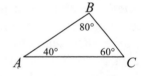

Additive Inverse Property   The additive inverse property states that for every number a there is a number $-a$ such that $a + (-a) = 0$. For example, the number 5 has an additive inverse of -5; $5 + (-5) = 0$. The additive inverse of a number is often called its opposite. For example, 5 and -5 are opposites.

adjacent angles   For two angles to be adjacent, the angles must satisfy these three conditions: (1) the two angles must have a common side; (2) the two angles must have a common vertex; and (3) the two angles may have no interior points in common. Meeting these three conditions means that the common side must be between the two angles. No overlap between the angles is permitted. In the example at right, $\angle ABC$ and $\angle CBD$ are adjacent angles.

algebra   A branch of mathematics that uses variables to generalize the rules of numbers and numerical operations.

algebra tiles   An algebra tile is a manipulative whose
area represents a constant or variable quantity. The
algebra tiles used in this course consist of large squares
with dimensions x-by-x and y-by-y; rectangles with
dimensions x-by-1, y-by-1, and x-by-y; and small
squares with dimensions 1-by-1. These tiles are named
by their areas: x^2, y^2, x, y, xy, and 1, respectively. The
smallest squares are called "unit tiles." In this text,
shaded tiles will represent positive quantities while
unshaded tiles will represent negative quantities.

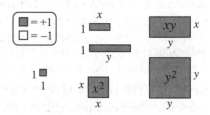

algebraic expression   See *expression*.

algorithm   A fixed rule for carrying out a mathematical procedure. For example, to find
the average of a set of values, find the sum of the values and divide by the number of
values.

altitude of a triangle   The length of a segment that connects a vertex of the
triangle to a line containing the opposite base (side) and is perpendicular to
that line. (See *height*.)

angle   Generally, an angle is formed by two rays that
are joined at a common endpoint. Angles in geometric
figures are usually formed by two segments that have a
common endpoint (such as the angle shaded in the
figure at right). (Also see *acute angle*, *obtuse angle*,
and *right angle*.)

angle bisector   A ray that divides an angle into two congruent parts.

arc

arc   A part of a circle or curve between two points on the circle.

area   For this course, area is the number of square units needed to
fill up a region on a flat surface. In later courses, the idea will be
extended to cones, spheres, and more complex surfaces. (Also see
surface area.)

Area = 15 square units

area of a circle $A = \pi r^2$, where r is the length of the radius of the
circle. (See "circle.")

area of a triangle   To find the area of a triangle, multiply the length of the base b by the
height h and divide by two: $A = \frac{1}{2}bh$. (Also see *altitude of a triangle*.)

Associative Property for Addition   The associative property of addition states that if a
sum contains terms that are grouped, then the sum may be grouped differently with no
effect on the total, that is, $a + (b + c) = (a + b) + c$. For example, $3 + (4 + 5) = (3 + 4) + 5$.

Making Connections

Associative Property for Multiplication   The associative property of multiplication states that if a product contains terms that are grouped, then the product may be grouped differently with no effect on the result, that is, $a(bc) = (ab)c$. For example, $2 \cdot (3 \cdot 4) = (2 \cdot 3) \cdot 4$.

average   The sum of given values divided by the number of values used in computing the sum. For example, the average of 1, 4, and 10 is $(1 + 4 + 10) / 3$. (See *mean*.)

axis (plural: axes)   In a coordinate plane, two number lines that meet at right angles at the origin (0, 0). The x-axis runs horizontally and the y-axis runs vertically.

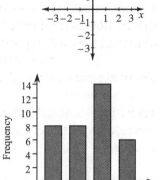

bar graph   A bar graph is a set of rectangular bars that have height proportional to the number of data elements in each category. Each bar stands for all of the elements in a single distinguishable category (such as "red"). Usually all of the bars are the same width and separated from each other. (Also see *histogram*.)

base of a geometric figure   (a) The base of a triangle: any side of a triangle to which a height is drawn. There are three possible bases in each triangle. (b) The base of a trapezoid: either of the two parallel sides. (c) The base of a parallelogram (including rectangle, rhombus, and square): any side to which a height is drawn. There are four possible bases. (d) The base of a solid: also see *cone*, *cylinder*, *prism*, and *pyramid*.

base of an exponent   When working with an exponential expression in the form a^b, a is called the base. For example, 2 is the base in 2^5. (5 is the exponent, and 32 is the value.) (Also see *exponent*.)

bimodal   A set of numbers that has two modes.

boundary point   The endpoint or endpoints of a ray or segment on a number line where an inequality is true. For strict inequalities (that is, inequalities involving < or >), the point is not part of the solution. Boundary points may be found by solving the equality associated with the given inequality. For example, the solution to the equation $2x + 5 = 11$ is $x = 3$, so the inequality $2x + 5 \geq 11$ has a boundary point at 3. The solution to that inequality is illustrated on the number line at right. A boundary point is also sometimes called a "dividing point."

box-and-whisker plot   A graphic way of showing a summary of data using the median, quartiles, and extremes of the data.

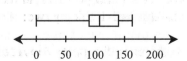

center (center point) Within a flat surface, the point that is the same distance from all points of a circle. (Also see *circle*.)

central angle An angle with its vertex at the center of a circle. (Also see *circle*.)

certainty When an event will definitely happen. The probability of a certain event is 1.

chord A line segment with its endpoints on a circle. A chord that passes through the center of a circle is called a "diameter." (Also see *circle*.)

circle The set of all points on a flat surface that are the same distance from a fixed point. If the fixed point (center) is O, then the symbol $\odot O$ represents a circle with center O. If r is the length of the radius of a circle and d is the length of its diameter, then the circumference of the circle is $C = 2\pi r$ or $C = \pi d$.

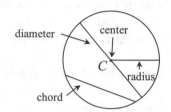

circumference The perimeter of (distance around) a circle. (Also see *circle*.)

coefficient (numerical) A number multiplying a variable or product of variables. For example, -7 is the coefficient of $-7xy^2$.

combining like terms Combining two or more like terms simplifies an expression by summing constants and summing those variable terms in which the same variables are raised to the same power. For example, combining like terms in the expression $3x + 7 + 5x - 3 + 2x^2 + 3y^2$ gives $8x + 4 + 2x^2 + 3y^2$. When working with algebra tiles, combining like terms involves putting together tiles with the same dimensions.

common Shared.

common factor A common factor is a factor that is the same for two or more terms. For example, x^2 is a common factor for $3x^2$ and $-5x^2y$.

common multiple A number that is a multiple of the two or more numbers. For example, 24 and 48 are common multiples of 3 and 8.

Commutative Property of Addition The Commutative Property of Addition states that if two terms are added, then the order may be reversed with no effect on the total. That is, $a + b = b + a$. For example, $7 + 12 = 12 + 7$.

Commutative Property of Multiplication The Commutative Property of Multiplication states that if two expressions are multiplied, then the order may be reversed with no effect on the result. That is, $ab = ba$. For example, $5 \cdot 8 = 8 \cdot 5$.

Making Connections

complementary angles Two angles whose measures add up to 90°. Angles T and V are complementary because $m\angle T + m\angle V = 90°$. Complementary angles may also be adjacent, like $\angle ABC$ and $\angle CBD$ in the diagram at far right.

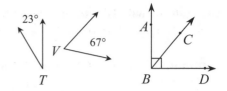

complementary probabilities Two probabilities are complementary if the sum of the probabilities is one.

complex fraction A fraction with a fraction in the numerator and/or denominator.

composite figure A shape made of several simpler figures.

composite number A number with more than two factors.

compound event A compound event in probability is an outcome that depends on two or more other events. For example, finding the probability that both a red ball and also a blue block are drawn from a bag in two draws.

compound interest Interest that is paid on both the principal and the previous interest earned which grows over time. Compound interest may be calculated using the formula $B = p(1 + r)^t$, in which B is the balance, p is the principal, r is the annual rate, and t is the time in years that the account earns interest.

cone A three-dimensional figure that consists of a circular face, called the "base," a point called the "apex," that is not in the flat surface (plane) of the base, and the slant surface that connects the apex to each point on the circular edge of the base.

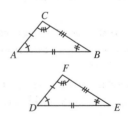

congruent Two shapes are congruent if they have exactly the same shape and size. Congruent shapes are similar and have a scale factor of 1. The symbol for congruence is $\cong$.

conjecture An educated guess that often results from noticing a pattern. Conjectures are also often written in conditional ("If…, then…") form. Once a conjecture is proven, then the conjecture becomes a theorem.

consecutive numbers Integers that are in order without skipping any integers. For example, 8, 9, and 10 are consecutive numbers.

constant A symbol representing a value that does not change. For example, in the equation $y = 2x + 5$, the number 5 is a constant.

construction with a compass and straightedge The process of using a straightedge and compass to solve a problem and/or create a geometric diagram.

coordinate The number corresponding to a point on the number line or an ordered pair (x, y) that corresponds to a point in a two-dimensional coordinate system. In an ordered pair, the x-coordinate appears first and the y-coordinate appears second. For example, the point $(3, 5)$ has an x-coordinate of 3. (See *ordered pair*.)

coordinate grid (system) A system of graphing ordered pairs of numbers on a coordinate plane. An ordered pair represents a point, with the first number giving the horizontal position relative to the x-axis and the second number giving the vertical position relative to the y-axis. (Also see *ordered pair*.)

correlation A measure of the relationship between two sets of data.

corresponding parts Points, sides, edges, or angles in two or more figures that are images of each other with respect to a transformation. If two figures are congruent, then the corresponding parts of the figures are congruent to each other. (See *ratio of similarity*.)

cube A polyhedron of six faces, each of which is a square.

cubic unit A cube, each of whose edges measure 1 unit in length. Volume is measured in cubic units.

cylinder A three-dimensional figure that consists of two parallel congruent circular regions (called *bases*) and a vertical surface containing segments connecting each point on the circular boundary of one base to the corresponding point on the circular boundary of the other.

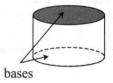

bases

decimal point The dot separating the whole number from the decimal portion, that is, the ones and tenths places in a decimal number.

decompose If a geometric figure is broken up into separate parts, then the figure is decomposed. Similarly, if a number is written as a sum or difference (such as $28 = 30 - 2$), then the number is decomposed. (Also see *recompose*.)

denominator The lower part of a fraction, which expresses into how many equal parts the whole is divided.

dependent events   Two events are dependent if the outcome of one event affects the probability of the other event. For example, if one card is drawn out of a deck of cards, then the probability that the first card is red is $\frac{26}{52} = \frac{1}{2}$ because 26 of the 52 cards are red. However, the probability of the second card now depends on the result of the first selection. If the first card was red, then there are now 25 red cards remaining in a deck of 51 cards, and the probability that the second card is red is $\frac{25}{51}$. The second event (selecting the second card) is dependent on the first event (selecting the first card).

diagonal   In a polygon, a diagonal is a line segment that connects two vertices of the polygon but is not a side of the polygon.

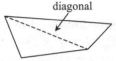
diagonal

diameter   A line segment drawn through the center of a circle with both endpoints on the circle. The length of a diameter is usually denoted d. Note that the length of the diameter of a circle is twice the length of its radius. (Also see *circle*.)

difference   The result of subtraction.

digit   One of the ten numerals: 0, 1, 2, 3, 4, 5, 6, 7, 8, or 9.

dilation   A transformation which produces a figure similar to the original by proportionally shrinking or stretching the figure. In a dilation, a shape is stretched (or compressed) proportionally from a point, called the point of dilation.

dimensions   The dimensions of a figure that is a flat region or space tell how far that the figure extends in each direction. For example, the dimensions of a rectangle might be 16 cm wide by 7 cm high.

Distributive Property   For any a, b, and c, $a(b+c) = ab + ac$. For example, $10(7+2) = 10 \cdot 7 + 10 \cdot 2$.

dividend   A quantity to be divided. (See *divisor*.)

divisible   A number is divisible by another if the remainder of the division is zero.

division ($\div$)   The inverse operation to multiplication, or the operation that creates equal groups.

divisor   The quantity by which another quantity is to be divided.
dividend/divisor = quotient + remainder (if there is any).

edge   In three dimensions, a line segment formed by the intersection of two faces of a polyhedron.

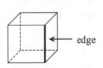
edge

endpoint   Either of the two points that mark the ends of a line segment. (Also see *line segment*.)

enlargement ratio   The ratio of similarity comparing a figure to a similar larger figure is often called the enlargement ratio. This ratio shows by what factor the first figure is enlarged to get the second figure.

equal (=)   Two quantities are equal when they have the same value. For example, when $x = 4$, the expression $x + 8$ is equal to the expression $3x$ because the values of the expressions are the same.

equal ratios   Two equivalent fractions, also called a proportion. For example, $\frac{40 \text{ miles}}{2 \text{ gallons}} = \frac{100 \text{ miles}}{50 \text{ gallons}}$.

equation   A mathematical sentence in which two expressions appear on either side of an "equals" sign (=), stating that the two expressions are equivalent. For example, the equation $7x + 4.2 = -8$ states that the expression $7x + 4.2$ has the value -8. In this course, an equation is often used to represent a rule relating two quantities. For example, a rule for finding the area y of a tile pattern with figure number x might be written $y = 4x - 3$.

equilateral   A polygon is equilateral if all of its sides have equal length. The word "equilateral" comes from "equi" (meaning "equal") and "lateral" (meaning "side"). Equilateral triangles not only have sides of equal length, but also angles of equal measure. However, a polygon with more than three sides may be equilateral without having congruent angles. For example, see the rhombus at right.

equivalent   Two expressions are equivalent if they have the same value. For example, $2 + 3$ is equivalent to $1 + 4$. Two equations are equivalent if they have all the same solutions. For example, $y = 3x$ is equivalent to $2y = 6x$. Equivalent equations also have the same graph.

equivalent fractions   Two fractions are equivalent if they have the same numerical value. For example, 3/6 and 5/10 are equivalent fractions.

evaluate (an expression)   To find the numerical value of. To evaluate an expression, substitute the value(s) given for the variable(s) and perform the operations according to the order of operations. For example, evaluating $2x + y - 10$ when $x = 4$ and $y = 3$ gives the value 1. (Also see *expression*.)

even number   A whole number that is divisible by two with no remainder.

event   One or more results of an experiment.

experimental probability   The probability based on data collected in experiments. The experimental probability of an event is defined to be $\frac{\text{number of successful outcomes in the experiment}}{\text{total number of outcomes in the experiment}}$.

exponent   In an expression of the form a^b, b is called the exponent. For example, in the expression 2^5, 5 is called the exponent (2 is the base, and 32 is the value). The exponent indicates how many times to use the base as a multiplier. For example, in 2^5, 2 is used 5 times: $2^5 = 2 \cdot 2 \cdot 2 \cdot 2 \cdot 2 = 32$. For exponents of zero, the rule is: for any number $x \neq 0$, $x^0 = 1$.

expression   An expression is a combination of individual terms separated by plus or minus signs. For example, if each of the following terms, $6xy^2$, 24, and $\frac{y-3}{4+x}$, are combined into an expression, the result may be $6xy^2 + 24 - \frac{y-3}{4+x}$. An expression does not have an "equals" sign.

expression mat   An organizing tool used to visually represent an expression with algebra tiles. An expression mat has two regions, a positive region at the top and a negative region at the bottom. The tiles on the expression mat at right represent a value of –3.

Value: –3

face   One of the flat surfaces of a polyhedron, including the base(s).

factor   (1) In arithmetic: when two or more integers are multiplied, each of the integers is a factor of the product. For example, 4 is a factor of 24, because $4 \cdot 6 = 24$.
(2) In algebra: when two or more algebraic expressions are multiplied together, each of the expressions is a factor of the product. For example, x^2 is a factor of $-17x^2y^3$, because $(x^2)(-17y^3) = -17x^2y^3$. (3) To factor an expression is to write the expression as a product. For example, the factored form of $x^2 - 3x - 18$ is $(x - 6)(x + 3)$.

family of fractions   All fractions that are equivalent to each other form a family of fractions. (See *equivalent fractions*.)

formula   An equation that shows a mathematical relationship.

fraction   A number expressed in the form $\frac{a}{b}$ for which a and b are integers and b is not equal to 0. A fraction is also called a rational number.

frequency   The number of times that something occurs within an interval or data set.

generic rectangle   A type of diagram used to visualize multiplying expressions without algebra tiles. Each expression to be multiplied forms a side length of the rectangle, and the product is the sum of the areas of the sections of the rectangle. For example, the generic rectangle at right may be used to multiply $(2x + 5)$ by $(x + 3)$.

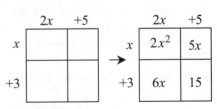

$$(2x + 5)(x + 3) = 2x^2 + 11x + 15$$

area as a product   area as a sum

graph   A graph represents numerical information in a visual form. The numbers may come from a table, situation (pattern), or rule (equation or inequality). Most of the graphs in this course show points, lines, and/or curves on a two-dimensional coordinate system like the one at right or on a single axis called a number line (see diagram below right).

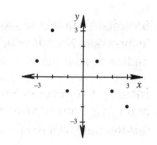

greatest common factor (GCF)   (1) For integers, the greatest positive integer that is a common factor of two or more integers. For example, the greatest common factor of

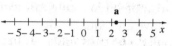

28 and 42 is 14. (2) For two or more algebraic monomials, the product of the greatest common integer factor of the coefficients of the monomials and the variable(s) in each algebraic term with the smallest degree of that variable in every term. For example, the greatest common factor of $12x^3y^2$ and $8xy^4$ is $4xy^2$. (3) For a polynomial, the greatest common monomial factor of its terms. For example, the greatest common factor of $16x^4 + 8x^3 + 12x$ is $4x$.

height   (a) Triangle: the length of a segment that connects a vertex of the triangle to a line containing the opposite base (side) and is perpendicular to that line. (b) Trapezoid: the length of any segment that connects a point on one base of the trapezoid to the line containing the opposite base and is perpendicular to that line. (c) Parallelogram (includes rectangle, rhombus, and square): the length of any segment that connects a point on one base of the parallelogram to the line containing the opposite base and is perpendicular to that line. (d) Pyramid and cone: the length of the segment that connects the apex to a point in the plane containing the base of a figure and is perpendicular to that plane. (e) Prism or cylinder: the length of a segment that connects one base of the figure to the plane containing the other base and is perpendicular to that plane. (See *altitude*.)

hexagon   A polygon with six sides.

histogram   A way of displaying data that is much like a bar graph in that the height of the bars is proportional to the number of elements. The difference is that each bar of a histogram represents the number of data elements in a range of values, such as the number of people who weigh from 100 pounds up to, but not including, 120 pounds. Each range of values should have the same width. (See *bar graph*.)

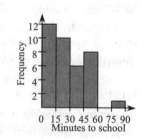

horizontal   Parallel to the horizon. The *x*-axis of a coordinate grid is the horizontal axis.

hypotenuse   The longest side of a right triangle (the side that is opposite of the right angle). (See *Pythagorean Theorem* for a diagram.)

Identity Property of Addition The Identity Property of Addition states that adding zero to any expression leaves the expression unchanged. That is, $a + 0 = a$. For example, $-2y + 0 = -2y$.

Identity Property of Multiplication The Identity Property of Multiplication states that multiplying any expression by 1 leaves the expression unchanged. That is, $a(1) = a$. For example, $437x \cdot 1 = 437x$.

impossibility An event with a probability of zero.

independent events If the outcome of a probabilistic event does not affect the probability of another event, then the events are independent. For example, assume that a normal six-sided die is being rolled twice to determine the probability of rolling a 1 twice. The result of the first roll does not affect the probability of rolling a 1 on the second roll. Since the probability of rolling a 1 on the first roll is $\frac{1}{6}$ and the probability of rolling a 1 on the second roll is also $\frac{1}{6}$, then the probability of rolling two 1s in a row is $\frac{1}{6} \cdot \frac{1}{6} = \frac{1}{36}$.

inequality An inequality consists of two expressions on either side of an inequality symbol. For example, the inequality $7x + 4.2 < -8$ states that the expression $7x + 4.2$ has a value less than -8.

inequality symbols The symbol $\leq$ read from left to right means "less than or equal to," the symbol $\geq$ read from left to right means "greater than or equal to," and the symbols $<$ and $>$ mean "less than" and "greater than," respectively. For example, "$7 < 13$" means that 7 is less than 13.

integers The set of numbers $\{..., -3, -2, -1, 0, 1, 2, 3, ...\}$.

intersect To meet or cross. The x-axis intersects the y-axis at the origin. (See *axis*.)

interval A set of numbers between two given numbers.

inverse operation An operation that undoes another operation. For example, multiplication is the inverse operation for division.

irrational numbers The set of numbers that cannot be expressed in the form $\frac{a}{b}$, where a and b are integers and $b \neq 0$. For example, π and $\sqrt{2}$ are irrational numbers.

isosceles triangle A triangle with two sides of equal length.

iterate The process of repeating a measurement many times, such as the use of a one-foot ruler to measure a long room by placing the ruler end-to-end many times.

kite A quadrilateral with two distinct pairs of consecutive congruent sides.

least common multiple (LCM)   (1) The smallest common multiple of a set of two or more integers. For example, the least common multiple of 4, 6, and 8 is 24.   (2) For two or more algebraic monomials, the product of the least common integer multiples of the coefficients of the monomials and the variable(s) in each algebraic term with the greatest degree of that variable in every term. For example, the least common factor of $12x^3y^2$ and $8xy^4$ is $24x^3y^4$.

leg of a right triangle   Either of the two shorter sides of a right triangle that form the right angle. (See *Pythagorean Theorem* for a diagram.)

less than   (1) One expression is less than another if its value is not as large. This relationship is indicated with the less than symbol "$<$." For example, $1+1$ is less than $4+5$, so the comparison is written as $1+1<4+5$.   (2) Sometimes the comparison is made that one amount is a certain quantity less than another amount. For example, a student movie ticket might cost two dollars *less than* an adult ticket.

like terms   Two or more terms that contain the same variable(s), with corresponding variables raised to the same power. For example, $5x^2$ and $2x^2$ are like terms. (See *combining like terms*.)

line   A line is an undefined term in geometry. A line is one-dimensional and continues without end in two directions. A line is made up of points and has no thickness. A line may be named with a letter (such as l), but also may be labeled using two points on the line, such as $\overleftrightarrow{AB}$ shown the right.

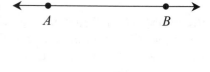

line segment   The portion of a line between two points. A line segment is named using its endpoints. For example, the line segment at right may be named either $\overline{AB}$ or $\overline{BA}$.

linear equation   An equation in two variables whose graph is a line. For example, $y=2.1x-8$ is a *linear equation*. The standard form for a linear equation is $ax+by=c$, where a, b, and c are constants and a and b are not both zero. Most linear equations may be written in $y=mx+b$ form, which is more useful for determining the slope and y-intercept of the line.

linear expression   An expression in the form of $ax+b$ for which a and b are numbers.

lower quartile   The median of the lower half of an ordered set of data is the lower quartile.

lowest common denominator (LCD)   The smallest common multiple of the denominators of two or more fractions. For example, the LCD of $\frac{5}{12}$ and $\frac{3}{8}$ is 24.

mean   The mean, or average, of several numbers is one way of defining the "middle" of the numbers. To find the average of a group of numbers, add the numbers together then divide by the number of numbers in the set. For example, the average of the numbers 1, 5, and 6 is $(1+5+6) \div 3 = 4$. (See *average*.)

measure of central tendency   Mean, median, and mode are all measures of central tendency, reflecting special statistical information about a set of data.

median   The middle number of an ordered set of data. If there is no distinct middle, then the average of the two middle numbers is the median.

midpoint   A point that divides a segment into two segments of equal length. For example, D is the midpoint of $\overline{BC}$ in $\triangle ABC$ at right.

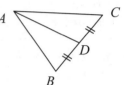

mixed number (fraction)   A number that consists of an integer and a fraction. For example, $3\frac{3}{8}$.

mode   The number or numbers that occur the most often within a set of data. There may be more than one mode for a set of data.

multiple   The product of a whole number and any other (nonzero) whole number. For example, 15 is a multiple of 5.

multiplication ($\cdot$)   An operation that reflects repeated addition. For example, $3 \cdot 4 = 4 + 4 + 4$.

multiplicative identity   The multiplicative identity property states that multiplying any expression by 1 leaves the expression unchanged. That is, $a(1) = a$. For example, $437x \cdot 1 = 437x$.

natural numbers   The counting numbers beginning with 1. For example, 1, 2, 3….

negative correlation   A relationship between two sets of variables in which one generally increases while the other decreases.

negative number   A negative number is a number less than zero. Negative numbers are graphed on the negative side of a number line, which is to the left of the origin.

negative slope   Lines are said to have negative slope if they slant downward from left to right. That is, as the x-values increases, the y-value decreases.

non-linear   A set of points that do not lie on a straight line when connected.

Glossary

number line A diagram representing all real numbers as points on a line. All real numbers are assigned to points. The numbers are called the coordinates of the points and the point for which the number 0 is assigned is called the origin. (Also see *boundary point*.)

numeral A symbol that names a number. For example, each item of the following list is a numeral: 22.6, –19, 0.

numerator The number above the bar in a fraction that tells the numbers of parts in relationship to the number of parts in the whole.

obtuse angle Any angle that measures between (but not including) 90° and 180°.

obtuse triangle A triangle with one obtuse angle.

octagon A polygon with eight sides.

odd number An integer that cannot be evenly divided by two.

operation A mathematical process such as addition, subtraction, multiplication, division, raising to a power, or taking a root.

order of operations The specific order in which certain operations are to be carried out to evaluate or simplify expressions: parentheses (or other grouping symbols), exponents (powers or roots), multiplication and division (from left to right), and addition and subtraction (from left to right).

ordered pair Two numbers written in order as follows: (x, y). The primary use of ordered pairs in this course is to represent points in an xy-coordinate system. The first coordinate (x) represents the horizontal distance from the origin. The second coordinate (y) represents the vertical distance from the origin. For example, the ordered pair $(3, 5)$ represents the point shown in bold at right.

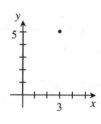

origin The point on a coordinate plane where the x-axis and y-axis intersect is called the origin. This point has coordinates $(0, 0)$. The point assigned to zero on a number line is also called the origin. (See *axis*.)

outcome Possible result in an experiment or consequence of an action.

outlier A number in a set of data that is much larger or much smaller than the other numbers in the set.

parallel   Two or more straight lines on a flat surface that do not intersect (no matter how far they are extended) are parallel. If two lines have the same slope and do not coincide, then they are parallel. For example, the graphs of $y = 2x + 3$ and $y = 2x - 2$ are parallel (see diagram at right). When two equations have parallel graphs, the equations have no solutions in common.

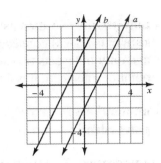

parallelogram   A quadrilateral with two pairs of parallel sides.

pentagon   A polygon with five sides.

percent (%)   A ratio that compares a number to 100. Percents are often written using the "%" symbol. For example, 0.75 is equal to $\frac{75}{100}$ or 75%.

perfect square   The product of an integer multiplied by itself gives a perfect square. For example, 1, 4, and 9 are perfect squares because $1 = 1 \cdot 1$, $4 = 2 \cdot 2$, and $9 = 3 \cdot 3$.

Perimeter =
$5 + 8 + 4 + 6 = 23$ units

perimeter   The distance around a figure on a flat surface.

perpendicular   Two rays, line segments, or lines that meet (intersect) to form a right angle (90°) are called perpendicular. A line and a flat surface may also be perpendicular if the line does not lie on the flat surface but intersects the surface and forms a right angle with every line on the flat surface passing through the point of intersection. A small square at the point of intersection of two lines or segments indicates that the lines form a right angle and are therefore perpendicular.

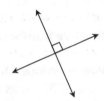

perpendicular bisector   A line, ray, or segment that divides a segment into two congruent segments and is perpendicular to the segment.

pi (π)   The ratio of the circumference (C) of the circle to its diameter (d). For every circle, $\pi = \frac{\text{circumference}}{\text{diameter}} = \frac{C}{d}$. Numbers such as 3.14, 3.1416, or $\frac{22}{7}$ are approximations of π.

place value   The number assigned to each place that a digit occupies.

plane.   A plane is a two-dimensional flat surface that extends without end. It is made up of points and has no thickness.

point   An exact location in space. In two dimensions, an ordered pair specifies a point on a coordinate plane. (See *ordered pair*.)

polygon   A two-dimensional closed figure of three or more line segments (sides) connected end to end. Each segment is a side and only intersects the endpoints of its two adjacent sides. Each point of intersection is a vertex. At right are two examples of polygons.

polyhedron   A three-dimensional figure with no holes for which all faces are polygons.

population   A collection of objects or group of people about whom information is gathered.

portion   A part of something; a part of a whole.

portions web   The web diagram at right illustrates that fractions, decimals, and percents are different ways to represent a portion of a number. Portions may also be represented in words, such as "four-fifths" or "seven-fourths," or as diagrams.

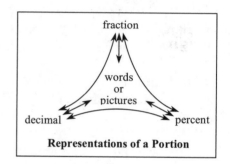

Representations of a Portion

positive correlation   A relationship between two sets of variables in which one generally increases while the other also increases.

positive numbers   Numbers that are greater than zero.

positive slope   Lines are said to have positive slope if they slant upwards from left to right. That is, as the x-value increases, the y-value also increases.

power   A number or variable raised to an exponent in the form x^n. (See *exponent*.)

prime factorization   The expression of a number as the product of prime factors.

prime number   A positive integer with exactly two factors. The only factors of a prime number are 1 and itself. For example, the numbers 2, 3, 17, and 31 are all prime.

prism   A three-dimensional figure that consists of two parallel congruent polygons (called *bases*) and a vertical surface containing segments connecting each point on each side of one base to the corresponding point on the other base. The lateral surface of a prism consists of parallelograms.

probability   A number that represents how likely an event is to happen. When a event has a finite number of equally-likely outcomes, the probability that one of those outcomes, called A, will occur is expressed as a ratio and written as: $P(A) = \frac{\text{number of successful outcomes}}{\text{total number of possible outcomes}}$. For example, when flipping a coin, the probability of getting tails, $P(\text{tails})$, is 1/2 because there is only one tail (successful outcome) out of the two possible equally likely outcomes (a head and a tail). Probability may be written as a ratio, decimal, or percent. A probability of 0 (or 0%) indicates that the occurrence of that outcome is impossible, while a probability of 1 (or 100%) indicates that the event must occur. Events that "might happen" will have values somewhere between 0 and 1 (or between 0% and 100%).

product   The result of multiplying. For example, the product of 4 and 5 is 20. The product of $3a$ and $8b^2$ is $24ab^2$.

proportion   An equation stating that two ratios (fractions) are equal. For example, the equation at right is a proportion. A proportion is a useful type of equation to set up when solving problems involving proportional relationships.

$$\frac{68 \text{ votes for Mr. Mears}}{100 \text{ people surveyed}} = \frac{34 \text{ votes for Mr. Mears}}{50 \text{ people surveyed}}$$

proportional relationship   Two values are in a proportional relationship if a proportion may be set up that relates the values.

protractor   A geometric tool used for physically measuring the number of degrees in an angle.

pyramid   A polyhedron with a polygonal base formed by connecting each point of the base to a single given point (the apex) that is above or below the flat surface containing the base. Each triangular slant face of the pyramid is formed by the segments from the apex to the endpoints of a side of the base and the side itself. A tetrahedron is a special pyramid because any face may act as its base.

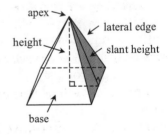

Pythagorean Theorem   The statement relating the lengths of the legs of a right triangle to the length of the hypotenuse: $(\text{leg \#1})^2 + (\text{leg \#2})^2 = \text{hypotenuse}^2$. The Pythagorean Theorem is powerful because if the lengths of any two sides of a right triangle are known, then this relationship may be used to find the length of the third side.

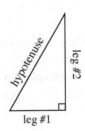

quadrants The coordinate plane is divided by its axes into four quadrants. The quadrants are numbered as shown in the first diagram at right. When graphing data that has no negative values, sometimes a graph that shows only the first quadrant is used.

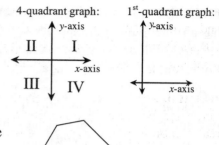

quadrilateral A polygon with four sides. The shape at right is a quadrilateral.

quartile Along with the median, the quartiles divide a set of data into four groups of the same size.

quotient The result of a division problem.

radius (plural: radii) Of a circle: The line segment drawn from the center of a circle to a point on the circle. Of a regular polygon: A line segment that connects the center of a regular polygon with a vertex. The length of a radius is usually denoted r.

random sample A sample in which each item in the population or sample space has an equal chance of being selected.

range The range of a set of data is the difference between the highest and lowest values.

rate A ratio comparing two quantities, often a comparison of time. For example, miles per hour.

ratio A ratio compares two quantities by division. A ratio may be written using a colon, but is more often written as a fraction. For example, the comparison may be made of the ratio of female students in a particular school to the total number of students in the school. This ratio could be written as 1521:2906 or as the fraction shown at right.

$$\frac{1521 \text{ female students}}{2906 \text{ total students}}$$

ratio of similarity The ratio of any pair of corresponding sides of two similar figures. This means that once it may be determined that two figures are similar, all of the pairs of corresponding sides of the figures have the same ratio. For example, for the similar triangles $\triangle ABC$ and $\triangle DEF$ at right, the ratio of similarity is $\frac{5}{11}$. The ratio of similarity may also be called the linear scale factor.

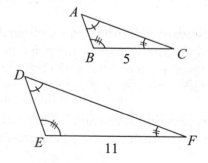

rational number Numbers that may be expressed in the form $\frac{a}{b}$, where a and b are integers and $b \neq 0$. For example, 0.75 is a rational number because 0.75 may be expressed in the form $\frac{3}{4}$.

ray   A ray is part of a line that starts at one point and extends without end in one direction. In the example at right, ray $\overrightarrow{AB}$ is part of line $\overleftrightarrow{AB}$ that starts at A and contains all of the points of $\overleftrightarrow{AB}$ that are on the same side of A as point B, including A. Point A is the endpoint of $\overrightarrow{AB}$.

real numbers   Irrational numbers together with rational numbers form the set of the real numbers. For example, the following are all real numbers: $2.78, -13267, 0, \frac{3}{7}, \pi, \sqrt{2}$. All real numbers are represented on the number line.

reciprocals   The reciprocal of a nonzero number is its multiplicative inverse, that is, the reciprocal of x is $\frac{1}{x}$. For a number in the form $\frac{a}{b}$, where a and b are non-zero, the reciprocal is $\frac{b}{a}$. The product of a number and its reciprocal is 1. For example, the reciprocal of 12 is $\frac{1}{12}$, because $12 \cdot \frac{1}{12} = 1$.

recompose   If a geometric figure is broken up into pieces and the pieces are put back together, possibly in a new way, then the figure is recomposed. Similarly, if two or more numbers have been written as sums or differences in an expression and these numbers are put back together into sums or differences, then the expression is recomposed. (Also see *decompose*.)

rectangle   A quadrilateral with four right angles.

reduce   To put a fraction into simplest form.

reflection   A transformation across a line that produces a mirror image of the original (pre-image) shape. The reflection is called the "image" of the original figure. The line is called a "line of reflection." Note that a reflection is also sometimes referred to as a "flip." See the example at right above.

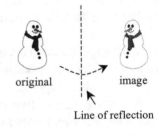

original   image

Line of reflection

regular polygon   A polygon is regular if the polygon is a convex polygon with congruent angles and congruent sides. For example, the shape at right is a regular hexagon.

REGULAR HEXAGON

repeating decimal   A repeating decimal is a decimal that repeats the same sequence of digits forever from some point onward. For example, 4.56073073073… is a decimal for which the three digits 073 continue to repeat forever. Repeating decimals are always the decimal expansions of rational numbers.

representative sample   A subset (group) of a given population with the same characteristics as the whole population.

rhombus   A quadrilateral with four congruent sides. (Also see *equilateral*.)

right angle   An angle that measures 90°. A small square is used to note a right angle, as shown in the example at right.

right triangle   A triangle that has one right angle. The side of a right triangle opposite the right angle is called the "hypotenuse," and the two sides adjacent to the right angle are called "legs." (See *Pythagorean Theorem* for a diagram.)

rigid transformations   Movements of figures that preserve the shape and size of the figures.

root fraction   The member of a family of fractions with the smallest integer values, the most simplified form. For the fraction family $\frac{2}{3}, \frac{4}{6}, \frac{6}{9}$, etc., $\frac{2}{3}$ is the root fraction.

rotation   A transformation that rotates (or turns) all of the points in the original (pre-image) figure the same number of degrees around a fixed center point (such as the origin on a graph). The result is called the "image" of the original figure. The point that the shape is rotated about is called the "center of rotation." To define a rotation, the measure of turn (in degrees) must be stated, the direction in which the shape is turned (such as clockwise or counter-clockwise), and the center of rotation. See the example at right. Note that a rotation is also sometimes referred to as a "turn."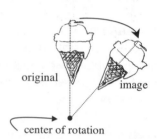

scale (scaling)   The ratio between a length of the representation (such as a map, model, or diagram) and the corresponding length of the actual object. For example, the map of a city may use one inch to represent one mile.

scale factor   A ratio that compares the sizes of the parts of one figure or object to the sizes of the corresponding parts of a similar figure or object.

scalene triangle   A triangle with no congruent sides.

scatterplot   Two related sets of data may have the corresponding values of the sets listed as ordered pairs. If these ordered pairs are graphed in the coordinate plane, then the result is a scatterplot. (Also see *negative correlation* and *positive correlation*.)

scientific notation   A number is expressed in scientific notation when the number is in the form $a \cdot 10^n$, where $1 \le a < 10$ and n is an integer. For example, the number 31,000 may be expressed in scientific notation as $3.1 \cdot 10^4$.

sector   A region formed by two radii of a central angle and the arc between the endpoints of the radii on the circle. The shaded portion of the drawing at right is a sector.

semi-circle   In a circle, a semicircle is an arc with endpoints that are endpoints of any diameter of the circle. A semi-circle is a half circle and has a measure of 180°.

set   A collection of items.

similar figures   Similar figures have the same shape but are not necessarily the same size. For example the two triangles at right are similar. In similar figures, the measures of corresponding angles are equal and the lengths of corresponding sides are proportional.

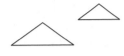

simple interest   Interest that is paid only on the principal (the amount originally invested). Simple interest is found by multiplying the principal, the rate, and the amount of time.

simplest form of a fraction   A fraction for which the numerator and the denominator have no common factor greater than one.

simplify   To simplify an expression is to write a less complicated expression with the same value. A simplified expression has no parentheses and no like terms. For example, the expression $3-(2x+7)-4x$ may be simplified to $-4-6x$. When working with algebra tiles, a simplified expression uses the fewest possible tiles to represent the original expression.

skew lines   Lines that do not lie in the same flat surface.

slope   A ratio that describes how steep (or flat) a line is. Slope may be positive, negative, or even zero, but a straight line has only one slope. Slope is the ratio $\frac{\text{vertical change}}{\text{horizontal change}}$ or $\frac{\text{change in } y\text{-value}}{\text{change in } x\text{-value}}$, sometimes written $\frac{\Delta y}{\Delta x}$. When the equation of a line is written in $y = mx + b$ form, m is the slope of the line. A line has positive slope if the line slopes upward from left to right on a graph, negative slope if the line slopes downward from left to right, zero slope if the line is horizontal, and undefined slope if the line is vertical. Parallel lines have equal slopes, and the slopes of perpendicular lines are opposite reciprocals of each other (e.g. $\frac{3}{5}$ and $-\frac{5}{3}$).

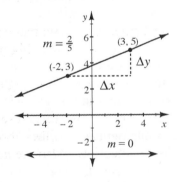

solution   The number or numbers that when substituted into an equation or inequality make the equation or inequality true. For example, $x = 4$ is a solution to the equation $3x - 2 = 10$ because $3x - 2$ equals 10 when $x = 4$. A solution to a two-variable equation is sometimes written as an ordered pair (x, y). For example, $x = 3$ and $y = -2$ is a solution to the equation $y = x - 5$. This solution may be written as $(3, -2)$.

square   A quadrilateral with four right angles and four congruent sides.

square

square measure   The units used to describe the measure of an area in the form of 1×1 unit squares.

square number   The numbers in the pattern 1, 4, 9, 16, 25, …. That is, the squares of the counting numbers 1, 2, 3, 4, 5, … are known as square numbers.

square root ($\sqrt{\ }$)   A number a is the square root of b if $a^2 = b$ and $a \geq 0$. The square root of 9 ($\sqrt{9}$) is 3. A negative number has no real square root, a non-negative number has just one square root.

stem-and-leaf plot   A way of displaying data values that is made by arranging the data with the vertical "stem" consisting of the first digits of the data and the horizontal "leaves" that show the remaining digits.

```
4 | 9
5 | 2  4  8
6 | 1  1  7  8
7 | 2  3  3  3  8
8 | 2  3
```
"stem"   "leaf"

straight angle   An angle that measures 180°. This occurs when the rays of the angle point in opposite directions, forming a line.

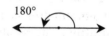
180°

subproblems   A problem solving strategy which breaks a problem into smaller parts which must be solved in order to solve the original, more complex problem.

substitution   Replacing one symbol with a number, a variable, or another algebraic expression of the same value. Substitution does not change the value of the overall expression. For example, suppose that the expression $13x - 6$ must be evaluated for $x = 4$. Since x has the value 4, 4 may be substituted into the expression wherever x appears, giving the equivalent expression $13(4) - 6$.

subtraction (–)   An operation that gives the difference between two numbers.

sum   The result of adding two or more numbers. For example, the sum of 4 and 5 is 9.

supplementary angles   Two angles A and B for which $A + B = 180°$. Each angle is called the supplement of the other. In the example at right, angles A and B are supplementary. Supplementary angles are often adjacent. For example, since $\angle LMN$ is a straight angle, then $\angle LMP$ and $\angle PMN$ are supplementary angles because $m\angle LMP + m\angle PMN = 180°$.

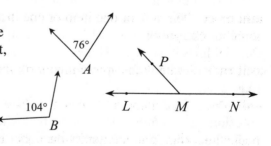

surface area   The sum of all the area(s) of the surface(s) of a three-dimensional solid. For example, the surface area of a cylinder is the sum of the areas of its top base, its bottom base, and its vertical or slant surfaces.

548

term A term is a single number, variable, or the product of numbers and variables, such as -45, $1.2x$, and $3xy^2$.

terminating decimal A terminating decimal is a decimal that has only a finite number of non-zero digits, such as 4.067. Terminating decimals are a particular kind of repeating decimal for which the repeating portion is zeros, so the example could be written 4.0670000000… but it is not necessary to write the zeros at the end.

tetrahedron A polyhedron with four faces.

theoretical probability A calculated probability based on the possible outcomes when each outcome has the same chance of occurring: (number of successful outcomes)/(total number of possible outcomes).

tick mark A symbol that shows that a number line has been divided into intervals of equal length. (See *number line*.)

translation A transformation that preserves the size, shape, and orientation of a figure while sliding (moving) it to a new location. The result is called the "image" of the original figure (pre-image). See the example at right. Note that a translation is sometimes referred to as a "slide."

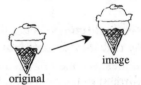

image

original

trapezoid A quadrilateral with at least one pair of parallel sides.

triangle A polygon with three sides.

unit of measure A standard quantity (such as a centimeter, second, square foot, or gallon) that is used to measure and describe an object. A single object may be measured using different units of measure. For example, a pencil may be 80 mm long, meaning that the pencil is 80 times as long as a unit of 1 mm. However, the same pencil is 8 cm long, so that the pencil is the same length as 8 cm laid end-to-end. This is because 1 cm is the same length as 10 mm.

unit price The cost of one item or one measure of an item. For example, cost for one pound or one gallon.

unit rate A rate with a denominator of one when simplified.

units digit The numeral in the ones place.

upper quartile The median of the upper half of an ordered set of data.

variable A symbol used to represent one or more numbers. In this course, letters of the English alphabet are used as variables. For example, in the expression $3x - (8.6xy + z)$, the variables are x, y, and z.

Venn diagram A type of diagram used to classify objects that is usually composed of two or more overlapping circles representing different condition. An item is placed or represented in the Venn diagram in the appropriate position based on the conditions that the item meets. In the example of the Venn diagram at right, if an object meets one of two conditions, then the object is placed in region *A* or *C* but outside region *B*. If an object meets both conditions, then the object is placed in the intersection (*B*) of both circles. If an object does not meet either condition, then the object is placed outside of both circles (region *D*).

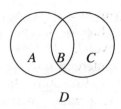

vertex (plural: vertices) (a) For polygon, a vertex is the point at which two line segments meet to form a "corner." (See *regular polygon*.) (b) For an angle, the common endpoint of the defining rays. (See *vertical angles*.) (c) For a three-dimensional polyhedron, a vertex is a point where the edges of the solid meet. (See *edge*.)

vertical At right angles to the horizon. In a coordinate grid, the *y*-axis runs vertically.

vertical angles The two opposite (that is, non-adjacent) angles formed by two intersecting lines. "Vertical" is a relationship between pairs of angles, so one angle cannot be called vertical. Angles that form a vertical pair are always congruent.

volume A measurement of the size of the three-dimensional region enclosed within an object. Volume is expressed as the number of $1 \times 1 \times 1$ unit cubes (or parts of cubes) that fit inside a solid.

x-axis The horizontal number line on a coordinate grid. (See *axis*.)

x-coordinate In an ordered pair, (p, q), that represents a point in the coordinate plane, p is the value of the *x*-coordinate of the point. That is, the horizontal distance from the origin that is needed to plot the point.

x-intercept The point(s) where a graph intersects the *x*-axis. A graph may have several *x*-intercepts, no *x*-intercepts, or just one. It is sometimes reported that the *x*-intercepts of a graph with coordinate pairs, but since the *y*-coordinate is always zero. Often just the *x*-coordinates of *x*-intercepts are given. (See *y-intercept*.)

y-axis The vertical number line on a coordinate grid. (See *axis*.)

y-coordinate In an ordered pair, (p, q), that represents a point in the coordinate plane, q is the value of the *y*-coordinate of the point. That is, the vertical distance from the origin that is needed to plot the point.

y-intercept   The point(s) where a graph intersects the y-axis. A function has at most one y-intercept while a relation may have several. The y-intercept of a graph is important because the y-intercept often represents the starting value of a quantity in a real-world situation. It is sometimes reported that the y-intercept of a graph with a coordinate pair, but since the x-coordinate is always zero, often just the y-coordinate of the y-intercept is given. For example, it may be said that that the y-intercept of the graph at right is $(0, 2)$, or it may also be said that the y-intercept is 2. When a linear equation is written in $y = mx + b$ form, b is the y-intercept of the graph. For example, the equation of the graph at right is $y = x + 2$ and its y-intercept is 2.

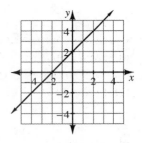

THIS BOOK IS THE PROPERTY OF:

Book No._____

ISSUED TO	Year Used	CONDITION	
		ISSUED	RETURNED

PUPILS to whom this texbook is issued must not write on any part of it in any way, unless otherwise instructed by the teacher.